Put a rocket under your revision with CGP!

GCSE Physics isn't the easiest subject on Earth, and that's putting it mildly.
Luckily, we've squeezed all the facts, theory and practical skills you'll need into this CGP book —
plus exam practice questions to put your new-found Physics knowledge to the test.

How to access your free Online Edition

This book includes a free Online Edition to read on your PC, Mac or tablet.
To access it, just go to **cgpbooks.co.uk/extras** and enter this code...

3383 6111 7189 2317

By the way, this code only works for one person. If somebody else has used
this book before you, they might have already claimed the Online Edition.

CGP — still the best! ☺

Our sole aim here at CGP is to produce the highest quality books —
carefully written, immaculately presented and dangerously close to being funny.

Then we work our socks off to get them out to you
— at the cheapest possible prices.

Contents

Published by CGP
From original material by Richard Parsons

Editors: Rachael Marshall, Sarah Oxley, Frances Rooney.
Contributors: Gemma Hallam and Paddy Gannon

ISBN: 978 1 78294 573 4

With thanks to Lucy Johnson and Karen Wells for the proofreading

With thanks to Ana Pungartnik for the copyright research.

Data used to construct stopping distance diagram on page 23 from the Highway Code. Contains public sector information licensed under the Open Government Licence v3.0. http://www.nationalarchives.gov.uk/doc/open-government-licence/version/3/

Printed by Elanders Ltd, Newcastle upon Tyne.
Clipart from Corel®
Illustrations by: Sandy Gardner Artist, email sandy@sandygardner.co.uk

Text, design, layout and original illustrations © Coordination Group Publications Ltd (CGP) 2016
All rights reserved.

The Scientific Method

This section isn't about how to 'do' science — but it does show you the way most scientists work.

Scientists Come Up With Hypotheses — Then Test Them

1) Scientists try to explain things. They start by observing something they don't understand.

2) They then come up with a hypothesis — a possible explanation for what they've observed.

3) The next step is to test whether the hypothesis might be right or not. This involves making a prediction based on the hypothesis and testing it by gathering evidence (i.e. data) from investigations. If evidence from experiments backs up a prediction, you're a step closer to figuring out if the hypothesis is true.

About 100 years ago, scientists hypothesised that atoms looked like this.

Several Scientists Will Test a Hypothesis

1) Normally, scientists share their findings in peer-reviewed journals, or at conferences.

2) Peer-review is where other scientists check results and scientific explanations to make sure they're 'scientific' (e.g. that experiments have been done in a sensible way) before they're published. It helps to detect false claims, but it doesn't mean that findings are correct — just that they're not wrong in any obvious way.

3) Once other scientists have found out about a hypothesis, they'll start basing their own predictions on it and carry out their own experiments. They'll also try to reproduce the original experiments to check the results — and if all the experiments in the world back up the hypothesis, then scientists start to think the hypothesis is true.

4) However, if a scientist does an experiment that doesn't fit with the hypothesis (and other scientists can reproduce the results) then the hypothesis may need to be modified or scrapped altogether.

After more evidence was gathered, scientists changed their hypothesis to this.

If All the Evidence Supports a Hypothesis, It's Accepted — For Now

1) Accepted hypotheses are often referred to as theories. Our currently accepted theories are the ones that have survived this 'trial by evidence' — they've been tested many times over the years and survived.

2) However, theories never become totally indisputable fact. If new evidence comes along that can't be explained using the existing theory, then the hypothesising and testing is likely to start all over again.

Now we think it's more like this.

Theories Can Involve Different Types of Models

1) A representational model is a simplified description or picture of what's going on in real life. Like all models, it can be used to explain observations and make predictions. E.g. the Bohr model of an atom is a simplified way of showing the arrangement of electrons in an atom (see p.49). It can be used to explain electron excitations in atoms.

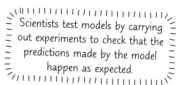

Scientists test models by carrying out experiments to check that the predictions made by the model happen as expected.

2) Computational models use computers to make simulations of complex real-life processes, such as climate change. They're used when there are a lot of different variables (factors that change) to consider, and because you can easily change their design to take into account new data.

3) All models have limitations on what they can explain or predict. E.g. the Big Bang model (a model used to describe the beginning of the Universe) can be used to explain why everything in the Universe is moving away from us. One of its limitations is that it doesn't explain the moments before the Big Bang.

I'm off to the zoo to test my hippo-thesis...

The scientific method has developed over time, and many people have helped to develop it. From Aristotle to modern day scientists, lots of people have contributed. And many more are likely to contribute in the future.

Communication & Issues Created by Science

Scientific developments can be great, but they can sometimes raise more questions than they answer...

It's Important to Communicate Scientific Discoveries to the General Public

Some scientific discoveries show that people should change their habits, or they might provide ideas that could be developed into new technology. So scientists need to tell the world about their discoveries.

> Radioactive materials are used widely in medicine for imaging and treatment (see p.56). Information about these materials needs to be communicated to doctors so they can make use of them, and to patients, so they can make informed decisions about their treatment.

Scientific Evidence can be Presented in a Biased Way

1) Reports about scientific discoveries in the media (e.g. newspapers or television) aren't peer-reviewed.

2) This means that, even though news stories are often based on data that has been peer-reviewed, the data might be presented in a way that is over-simplified or inaccurate, making it open to misinterpretation.

3) People who want to make a point can sometimes present data in a biased way. (Sometimes without knowing they're doing it.) For example, a scientist might overemphasise a relationship in the data, or a newspaper article might describe details of data supporting an idea without giving any evidence against it.

Scientific Developments are Great, but they can Raise Issues

Scientific knowledge is increased by doing experiments. And this knowledge leads to scientific developments, e.g. new technologies or new advice. These developments can create issues though. For example:

Economic issues: Society can't always afford to do things scientists recommend (e.g. investing in alternative energy sources) without cutting back elsewhere.

Personal issues: Some decisions will affect individuals. For example, someone might support alternative energy, but object if a wind farm is built next to their house.

Social issues: Decisions based on scientific evidence affect people — e.g. should fossil fuels be taxed more highly? Would the effect on people's lifestyles be acceptable...

Environmental issues: Human activity often affects the natural environment. For example, building a dam to produce electricity will change the local habitat so some species might be displaced. But it will also reduce our need for fossil fuels, so will help to reduce climate change.

Science Can't Answer Every Question — Especially Ethical Ones

1) We don't understand everything. We're always finding out more, but we'll never know all the answers.

2) In order to answer scientific questions, scientists need data to provide evidence for their hypotheses.

3) Some questions can't be answered yet because the data can't currently be collected, or because there's not enough data to support a theory.

4) Eventually, as we get more evidence, we'll answer some of the questions that currently can't be answered, e.g. what the impact of global warming on sea levels will be. But there will always be the "Should we be doing this at all?"-type questions that experiments can't help us to answer...

> Think about new drugs which can be taken to boost your 'brain power'.
>
> THE GAZETTE
> BRAIN-BOOSTING DRUGS MAKE A MOCKERY OF EXAMS
>
> THE POST
> GENIUS PILLS TO BECOME THE NEW COFFEE
>
> • Some people think they're good as they could improve concentration or memory. New drugs could let people think in ways beyond the powers of normal brains.
>
> • Other people say they're bad — they could give you an unfair advantage in exams. And people might be pressured into taking them so that they could work more effectively, and for longer hours.

Tea to milk or milk to tea? — Totally unanswerable by science...

Science can't tell you whether or not you should do something. That's for you and society to decide. But there are tons of questions science might be able to answer, like where life came from and where my superhero socks are.

Risk

By reading this page you are agreeing to the risk of a paper cut or severe drowsiness...

Nothing is Completely Risk-Free

1) A hazard is something that could potentially cause harm.

2) All hazards have a risk attached to them — this is the chance that the hazard will cause harm.

3) The risks of some things seem pretty obvious, or we've known about them for a while, like the risk of causing acid rain by polluting the atmosphere, or of having a car accident when you're travelling in a car.

4) New technology arising from scientific advances can bring new risks, e.g. scientists are unsure whether nanoparticles that are being used in cosmetics and suncream might be harming the cells in our bodies. These risks need to be considered alongside the benefits of the technology, e.g. improved sun protection.

5) You can estimate the size of a risk based on how many times something happens in a big sample (e.g. 100 000 people) over a given period (e.g. a year). For example, you could assess the risk of a driver crashing by recording how many people in a group of 100 000 drivers crashed their cars over a year.

6) To make decisions about activities that involve hazards, we need to take into account the chance of the hazard causing harm, and how serious the consequences would be if it did. If an activity involves a hazard that's very likely to cause harm, with serious consequences if it does, it's considered high risk.

People Make Their Own Decisions About Risk

1) Not all risks have the same consequences, e.g. if you chop veg with a sharp knife you risk cutting your finger, but if you go scuba-diving you risk death. You're much more likely to cut your finger during half an hour of chopping than to die during half an hour of scuba-diving. But most people are happier to accept a higher probability of an accident if the consequences are short-lived and fairly minor.

2) People tend to be more willing to accept a risk if they choose to do something (e.g. go scuba diving), compared to having the risk imposed on them (e.g. having a nuclear power station built next door).

3) People's perception of risk (how risky they think something is) isn't always accurate. They tend to view familiar activities as low-risk and unfamiliar activities as high-risk — even if that's not the case. For example, cycling on roads is often high-risk, but many people are happy to do it because it's a familiar activity. Air travel is actually pretty safe, but a lot of people perceive it as high-risk.

4) People may over-estimate the risk of things with long-term or invisible effects, e.g. ionising radiation.

Investigations Can be Hazardous

1) Hazards from science experiments might include:

> Hmm... why is this laser not working?

- Lasers, e.g. if a laser is directed into the eye, this can cause blindness.
- Gamma radiation, e.g. gamma-emitting radioactive sources can cause cancer.
- Fire, e.g. an unattended Bunsen burner is a fire hazard.
- Electricity, e.g. faulty electrical equipment could give you a shock.

2) Part of planning an investigation is making sure that it's safe.

3) You should always make sure that you identify all the hazards that you might encounter. Then you should think of ways of reducing the risks from the hazards you've identified. For example:

- If you're working with springs, always wear safety goggles. This will reduce the risk of the spring hitting your eye if the spring snaps.
- If you're using a Bunsen burner, stand it on a heat proof mat. This will reduce the risk of starting a fire.

> You can find out about potential hazards by looking in textbooks, doing some internet research, or asking your teacher.

Not revising — an unacceptable exam hazard...

The world's a dangerous place, but if you can recognise hazards, decide how to reduce their risks, and be happy to accept some risks, you can still have fun. Just maybe don't go skydiving with a great white shark on Friday 13th.

Designing Investigations

Dig out your lab coat and dust down your badly-scratched safety goggles... it's investigation time.

Investigations Produce Evidence to Support or Disprove a Hypothesis

1) Scientists observe things and come up with hypotheses to explain them (see p.2). You need to be able to do the same. For example:

> Observation: People with big feet have spots. Hypothesis: Having big feet causes spots.

2) To determine whether or not a hypothesis is right, you need to do an investigation to gather evidence. To do this, you need to use your hypothesis to make a prediction — something you think will happen that you can test. E.g. people who have bigger feet will have more spots.

3) Investigations are used to see if there are patterns or relationships between two variables, e.g. to see if there's a pattern or relationship between the variables 'number of spots' and 'size of feet'.

Evidence Needs to be Repeatable, Reproducible and Valid

1) Repeatable means that if the same person does an experiment again using the same methods and equipment, they'll get similar results.

2) Reproducible means that if someone else does the experiment, or a different method or piece of equipment is used, the results will still be similar.

3) If data is repeatable and reproducible, it's reliable and scientists are more likely to have confidence in it.

4) Valid results are both repeatable and reproducible AND they answer the original question. They come from experiments that were designed to be a FAIR TEST...

Investigations include experiments and studies.

To Make an Investigation a Fair Test You Have to Control the Variables

1) In a lab experiment you usually change one variable and measure how it affects another variable.

2) To make it a fair test, everything else that could affect the results should stay the same — otherwise you can't tell if the thing you're changing is causing the results or not.

3) The variable you CHANGE is called the INDEPENDENT variable.

4) The variable you MEASURE when you change the independent variable is the DEPENDENT variable.

5) The variables that you KEEP THE SAME are called CONTROL variables.

> You could find how current through a circuit component affects the potential difference (p.d.) across the component by measuring the p.d. at different currents. The independent variable is the current. The dependent variable is the potential difference. Control variables include the temperature of the component, the p.d. of the power supply, etc.

6) Because you can't always control all the variables, you often need to use a control experiment. This is an experiment that's kept under the same conditions as the rest of the investigation, but doesn't have anything done to it. This is so that you can see what happens when you don't change anything at all.

The Bigger the Sample Size the Better

1) Data based on small samples isn't as good as data based on large samples. A sample should represent the whole population (i.e. it should share as many of the characteristics in the population as possible) — a small sample can't do that as well. It's also harder to spot anomalies if your sample size is too small.

2) The bigger the sample size the better, but scientists have to be realistic when choosing how big. For example, if you were studying the effects of living near a nuclear power plant, it'd be great to study everyone who lived near a nuclear power plant (a huge sample), but it'd take ages and cost a bomb. It's more realistic to study a thousand people, with a mixture of ages, gender, and race.

This is no high street survey — it's a designer investigation...

Not only do you need to be able to plan your own investigations, you should also be able to look at someone else's plan and decide whether or not it needs improving. Those examiners aren't half demanding.

Collecting Data

You've designed the perfect investigation — now it's time to get your hands mucky and collect some data.

Your Data Should be Repeatable, Reproducible, Accurate and Precise

1) To check repeatability you need to repeat the readings and check that the results are similar. You need to repeat each reading at least three times.

2) To make sure your results are reproducible you can cross check them by taking a second set of readings with another instrument (or a different observer).

3) Your data also needs to be ACCURATE. Really accurate results are those that are really close to the true answer. The accuracy of your results usually depends on your method — you need to make sure you're measuring the right thing and that you don't miss anything that should be included in the measurements. E.g. estimating the volume of an irregularly shaped solid by measuring the sides isn't very accurate because this will not take into account any gaps in the object. It's more accurate to measure the volume using a density bottle (see p.93).

4) Your data also needs to be PRECISE. Precise results are ones where the data is all really close to the mean (average) of your repeated results (i.e. not spread out).

Beth's result was a curate.

Repeat	Data set 1	Data set 2
1	12	11
2	14	17
3	13	14
Mean	13	14

Data set 1 is more precise than data set 2.

Your Equipment has to be Right for the Job

1) The measuring equipment you use has to be sensitive enough to measure the changes you're looking for. For example, if you need to measure changes of 1 cm³ you need to use a measuring cylinder or burette that can measure in 1 cm³ steps — it'd be no good trying with one that only measures 10 cm³ steps.

2) The smallest change a measuring instrument can detect is called its RESOLUTION. E.g. some mass balances have a resolution of 1 g, some have a resolution of 0.1 g, and some are even more sensitive.

3) Also, equipment needs to be calibrated by measuring a known value. If there's a difference between the measured and known value, you can use this to correct the inaccuracy of the equipment.

You Need to Look out for Errors and Anomalous Results

1) The results of your experiment will always vary a bit because of RANDOM ERRORS — unpredictable differences caused by things like human errors in measuring. The errors when you make a reading from a ruler are random. You have to estimate or round the distance when it's between two marks — so sometimes your figure will be a bit above the real one, and sometimes it will be a bit below.

2) You can reduce the effect of random errors by taking repeat readings and finding the mean. This will make your results more precise.

3) If a measurement is wrong by the same amount every time, it's called a SYSTEMATIC ERROR. For example, if you measured from the very end of your ruler instead of from the 0 cm mark every time, all your measurements would be a bit small. Repeating your experiment in the exact same way and calculating a mean won't correct a systematic error.

If there's no systematic error, then doing repeats and calculating a mean can make your results more accurate.

4) Just to make things more complicated, if a systematic error is caused by using equipment that isn't zeroed properly, it's called a ZERO ERROR. For example, if a mass balance always reads 1 gram before you put anything on it, all your measurements will be 1 gram too heavy.

5) You can compensate for some systematic errors if you know about them though, e.g. if your mass balance always reads 1 gram before you put anything on it you can subtract 1 gram from all your results.

6) Sometimes you get a result that doesn't fit in with the rest at all. This is called an ANOMALOUS RESULT. You should investigate it and try to work out what happened. If you can work out what happened (e.g. you measured something totally wrong) you can ignore it when processing your results.

Watch what you say to that mass balance — it's very sensitive...

Weirdly, data can be really precise but not very accurate. For example, a fancy piece of lab equipment might give results that are really precise, but if it's not been calibrated properly those results won't be accurate.

Processing and Presenting Data

Processing your data means doing some <u>calculations</u> with it to make it <u>more useful</u>. Once you've done that, you can present your results in a nice <u>chart</u> or <u>graph</u> to help you <u>spot any patterns</u> in your data.

Data Needs to be Organised

1) Tables are dead useful for <u>organising data</u>.

2) When you draw a table <u>use a ruler</u> and make sure <u>each column</u> has a <u>heading</u> (including the <u>units</u>).

You Might Have to Process Your Data

1) When you've done repeats of an experiment you should always calculate the <u>mean</u> (average). To do this <u>add together</u> all the data values and <u>divide</u> by the total number of values in the sample.

2) You can also find the <u>mode</u> of your results — this is the <u>value</u> that <u>occurs</u> the <u>most</u> in your set of results.

3) The <u>median</u> can be found by writing your results in numerical <u>order</u> — the median is the <u>middle number</u>.

> Ignore anomalous results when calculating the mean, mode and median.

 **EXAMPLE:** The results of an experiment show the extension of spring A when a force is applied to it. Calculate the mean, mode and median of the extension for the spring.

Spring	Repeat (cm)					Mean (cm)	Mode (cm)	Median (cm)
	1	2	3	4	5			
A	18	26	22	26	28	(18 + 26 + 22 + 26 + 28) ÷ 5 = 24	26	26

Round to the Lowest Number of Significant Figures

The <u>first significant figure</u> of a number is the first digit that's <u>not zero</u>. The second and third significant figures come <u>straight after</u> (even if they're zeros). You should be aware of significant figures in calculations.

1) In <u>any</u> calculation, you should round the answer to the <u>lowest number of significant figures</u> (s.f.) given.

2) Remember to write down <u>how many</u> significant figures you've rounded to after your answer.

3) If your calculation has multiple steps, <u>only</u> round the <u>final</u> answer, or it won't be as accurate.

EXAMPLE: The mass of a solid is 0.24 g and its volume is 0.715 cm^3. Calculate the density of the solid.

$$\text{Density} = 0.24\ g \div 0.715\ cm^3 = 0.33566... = 0.34\ g/cm^3\ (2\ s.f.)$$

2 s.f.   3 s.f.   Final answer should be rounded to 2 s.f.

If Your Data Comes in Categories, Present It in a Bar Chart

1) If the independent variable is <u>categoric</u> (comes in distinct categories, e.g. solid, liquid, gas) you should use a <u>bar chart</u> to display the data.

2) You also use them if the independent variable is <u>discrete</u> (the data can be counted in chunks, where there's no in-between value, e.g. number of protons is discrete because you can't have half a proton).

3) You can also plot <u>continuous</u> data (see page 8).

There are some <u>golden rules</u> you need to follow for <u>drawing</u> bar charts:

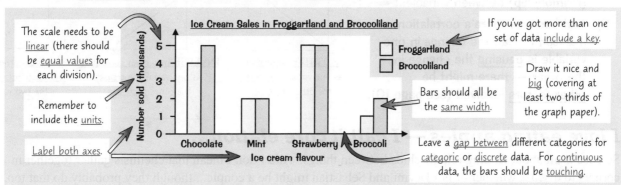

The scale needs to be <u>linear</u> (there should be <u>equal values</u> for each division).

Remember to include the <u>units</u>.

<u>Label both axes.</u>

If you've got more than one set of data <u>include a key</u>.

Draw it nice and <u>big</u> (covering at least two thirds of the graph paper).

Bars should all be the <u>same width</u>.

Leave a <u>gap between</u> different categories for <u>categoric</u> or <u>discrete</u> data. For <u>continuous</u> data, the bars should be <u>touching</u>.

Ice Cream Sales in Froggartland and Broccoliland — Number sold (thousands) — Chocolate, Mint, Strawberry, Broccoli — Ice cream flavour — Froggartland, Broccoliland

Graphs can be Used to Plot Continuous Data

If both variables are <u>continuous</u> (numerical data that can have any value within a range, e.g. length, volume, temperature) you can use a <u>graph</u> to display the data.

Here are the rules for plotting points on a graph:

Use the biggest data values you've got to draw a <u>sensible scale</u> on your axes. Here, the longest distance is <u>8.8 m</u>, so it makes sense to label the y-axis up to <u>10 m</u>.

The <u>dependent</u> variable goes on the <u>y-axis</u> (the <u>vertical</u> one).

The <u>independent</u> variable goes on the <u>x-axis</u> (the <u>horizontal</u> one).

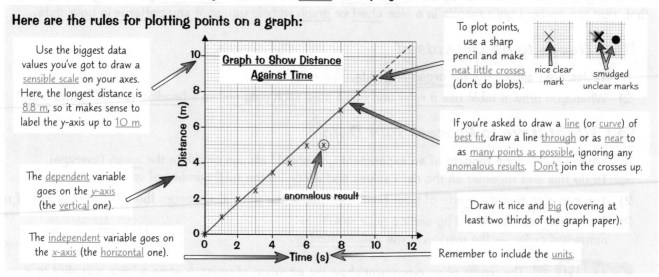

To plot points, use a sharp pencil and make <u>neat little crosses</u> (don't do blobs). nice clear mark / smudged unclear marks

If you're asked to draw a <u>line</u> (or <u>curve</u>) of <u>best fit</u>, draw a line <u>through</u> or as <u>near</u> to as <u>many points as possible</u>, ignoring any <u>anomalous results</u>. <u>Don't</u> join the crosses up.

Draw it nice and <u>big</u> (covering at least two thirds of the graph paper).

Remember to include the <u>units</u>.

Graphs Can Give You a Lot of Information About Your Data

1) The <u>gradient</u> (slope) of a graph tells you how quickly the <u>dependent variable</u> changes if you change the <u>independent variable</u>.

$$gradient = \frac{change\ in\ y}{change\ in\ x}$$

This <u>graph</u> shows the <u>distance travelled</u> by a vehicle against <u>time</u>. The graph is <u>linear</u> (it's a straight line graph), so you can simply calculate the <u>gradient</u> of the line to find out the <u>speed</u> of the vehicle.

1) To calculate the gradient, pick <u>two points</u> on the line that are easy to read and a <u>good distance</u> apart.

2) <u>Draw a line down</u> from one of the points and a <u>line across</u> from the other to make a <u>triangle</u>. The line drawn down the side of the triangle is the <u>change in y</u> and the line across the bottom is the <u>change in x</u>.

Change in y = 6.8 – 2.0 = 4.8 m   Change in x = 5.2 – 1.6 = 3.6 s

$$Rate = gradient = \frac{change\ in\ y}{change\ in\ x} = \frac{4.8\ m}{3.6\ s} = 1.3\ m/s$$

The units of the gradient are (units of y)/(units of x).

You can use this method to calculate other rates from a graph, not just the rate of change of distance (which is speed). Just remember that a rate is how much something changes over time, so x needs to be the time.

2) To find the <u>gradient of a curve</u> at a <u>certain point</u>, draw a <u>tangent</u> to the curve at that point and then find the <u>gradient of the tangent</u>. See page 14 for details on how to do this.

3) The <u>intercept</u> of a graph is where the line of best fit crosses one of the <u>axes</u>. The <u>x-intercept</u> is where the line of best fit crosses the x-axis and the <u>y-intercept</u> is where it crosses the <u>y-axis</u>.

Graphs Show the Relationship Between Two Variables

1) You can get <u>three</u> types of <u>correlation</u> (relationship) between variables:

2) Just because there's correlation, it doesn't mean the change in one variable is <u>causing</u> the change in the other — there might be <u>other factors</u> involved (see page 10).

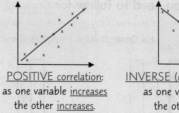

<u>POSITIVE</u> correlation: as one variable <u>increases</u> the other <u>increases</u>.

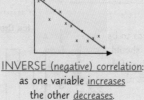

<u>INVERSE</u> (negative) correlation: as one variable <u>increases</u> the other <u>decreases</u>.

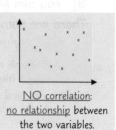

<u>NO</u> correlation: <u>no relationship</u> between the two variables.

I love eating apples — I call it core elation...

Science is all about finding relationships between things. And I don't mean that chemists gather together in corners to discuss whether or not Devini and Sebastian might be a couple... though they probably do that too.

Units and Equations

Graphs and maths skills are all very well, but the numbers don't mean much if you can't get the <u>units</u> right.

S.I. Units Are Used All Round the World

1) It wouldn't be all that useful if I defined volume in terms of <u>bath tubs</u>, you defined it in terms of <u>egg-cups</u> and my pal Sarwat defined it in terms of <u>balloons</u> — we'd never be able to compare our data.

2) To stop this happening, scientists have come up with a set of <u>standard units</u>, called S.I. units, that all scientists use to measure their data. Here are some S.I. units you'll see in physics:

Quantity	S.I. Base Unit
mass	kilogram, kg
length	metre, m
time	second, s
temperature	kelvin, K

Scaling Prefixes Can Be Used for Large and Small Quantities

1) Quantities come in a huge <u>range</u> of sizes. For example, the volume of a swimming pool might be around 2 000 000 000 cm^3, while the volume of a cup is around 250 cm^3.

2) To make the size of numbers more <u>manageable</u>, larger or smaller units are used. These are the <u>S.I. base unit</u> (e.g. metres) with a <u>prefix</u> in front:

prefix	tera (T)	giga (G)	mega (M)	kilo (k)	deci (d)	centi (c)	milli (m)	micro (μ)	nano (n)
multiple of unit	10^{12}	10^9	1 000 000 (10^6)	1000	0.1	0.01	0.001	0.000001 (10^{-6})	10^{-9}

3) These <u>prefixes</u> tell you <u>how much bigger</u> or <u>smaller</u> a unit is than the base unit. So one <u>kilometre</u> is <u>one thousand</u> metres.

The conversion factor is the number of times the smaller unit goes into the larger unit.

4) To <u>swap</u> from one unit to another, all you need to know is what number you have to divide or multiply by to get from the original unit to the new unit — this is called the <u>conversion factor</u>.

- To go from a <u>bigger unit</u> (like m) to a <u>smaller unit</u> (like cm), you <u>multiply</u> by the conversion factor.
- To go from a <u>smaller unit</u> (like g) to a <u>bigger unit</u> (like kg), you <u>divide</u> by the conversion factor.

5) Here are some conversions that'll be useful for GCSE physics:

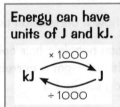

Mass can have units of kg and g.

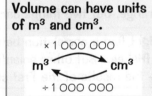

Energy can have units of J and kJ.

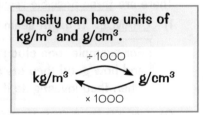

Volume can have units of m^3 and cm^3.

Density can have units of kg/m^3 and g/cm^3.

6) Numbers can also be written in <u>standard form</u>, e.g. 1×10^2 m = 100 m. Make sure you know how to work with standard form on <u>your calculator</u>.

Always Check The Values in Equations and Formulas Have the Right Units

1) Equations show <u>relationships</u> between <u>variables</u>.

2) To <u>rearrange</u> an equation — whatever you do to <u>one side</u> of the equation also do to the <u>other</u>.

wave speed = frequency × wavelength. You can <u>rearrange</u> this equation to find the <u>frequency</u> by <u>dividing each side</u> by wavelength to give: frequency = wave speed ÷ wavelength.

3) To use a formula, you need to know the values of <u>all but one</u> of the variables. <u>Substitute</u> the values you do know into the formula, and do the calculation to work out the final variable.

4) Always make sure the values you put into an equation or formula have the <u>right units</u>. For example, you might have done an experiment to find the speed of a trolley. The distance the trolley travels will probably have been measured in cm, but the equation to find speed uses distance in m. So you'll have to <u>convert</u> your distance from cm to m before you put it into the equation.

5) To make sure your units are <u>correct</u>, it can help to write down the <u>units</u> on each line of your <u>calculation</u>.

I wasn't sure I liked units, but now I'm converted...

It's easy to get in a muddle when converting between units, but there's a handy way to check you've done it right. If you're moving from a smaller unit to a larger unit (e.g. g to kg) the number should get smaller, and vice versa.

Drawing Conclusions

Congratulations — you're nearly at the end of a gruelling investigation, time to <u>draw conclusions</u>.

You Can Only Conclude What the Data Shows and NO MORE

1) Drawing conclusions might seem pretty straightforward — you just <u>look at your data</u> and <u>say what pattern or relationship you see</u> between the dependent and independent variables.

The table on the right shows the potential difference across a light bulb for three <u>different</u> currents through the bulb:

Current (A)	Potential difference (V)
6	4
9	10
12	13

<u>CONCLUSION:</u>
A <u>higher current</u> through the bulb gives a higher <u>potential difference</u> across the bulb.

2) But you've got to be really careful that your conclusion <u>matches the data</u> you've got and <u>doesn't go any further</u>. → You <u>can't</u> conclude that the potential difference across <u>any circuit component</u> will be higher for a larger current — the results might be completely different.

3) You also need to be able to <u>use your results</u> to <u>justify your conclusion</u> (i.e. back up your conclusion with some specific data). → The potential difference across the bulb was <u>9 V higher</u> with a current of 12 A compared to a current of 6 A.

4) When writing a conclusion you need to <u>refer back</u> to the original hypothesis and say whether the data <u>supports it</u> or not: → The hypothesis for this experiment might have been that a higher current through the bulb would <u>increase</u> the potential difference across the bulb. If so, the data <u>supports</u> the hypothesis.

Correlation DOES NOT Mean Cause

If two things are correlated (i.e. there's a relationship between them) it <u>doesn't</u> necessarily mean a change in one variable is <u>causing</u> the change in the other — this is <u>REALLY IMPORTANT</u> — <u>DON'T FORGET IT</u>. There are <u>three possible reasons</u> for a correlation:

1) <u>CHANCE:</u> It might seem strange, but two things can show a correlation purely due to <u>chance</u>.

For example, one study might find a correlation between people's hair colour and how good they are at frisbee. But other scientists <u>don't</u> get a correlation when they investigate it — the results of the first study are just a <u>fluke</u>.

2) <u>LINKED BY A 3RD VARIABLE:</u> A lot of the time it may <u>look</u> as if a change in one variable is causing a change in the other, but it <u>isn't</u> — a <u>third variable links</u> the two things.

For example, there's a correlation between <u>water temperature</u> and <u>shark attacks</u>. This isn't because warmer water makes sharks crazy. Instead, they're linked by a third variable — the <u>number of people swimming</u> (more people swim when the water's hotter, and with more people in the water you get more shark attacks).

3) <u>CAUSE:</u> Sometimes a change in one variable does <u>cause</u> a change in the other. You can only conclude that a correlation is due to cause when you've <u>controlled all the variables</u> that could, just could, be affecting the result.

For example, there's a correlation between <u>smoking</u> and <u>lung cancer</u>. This is because chemicals in tobacco smoke cause lung cancer. This conclusion was only made once <u>other variables</u> (such as age and exposure to other things that cause cancer) had been <u>controlled</u> and shown <u>not</u> to affect people's risk of getting lung cancer.

I conclude that this page is a bit dull...

...although, just because I find it dull doesn't mean that I can conclude it's dull (you might think it's the most interesting thing since that kid got his head stuck in the railings near school). In the exams you could be given a conclusion and asked whether some data supports it — so make sure you understand how far conclusions can go.

Uncertainties and Evaluations

Hurrah! The end of another investigation. Well, now you have to work out all the things you did <u>wrong</u>.

Uncertainty is the Amount of Error Your Measurements Might Have

1) When you <u>repeat</u> a measurement, you often get a <u>slightly different</u> figure each time you do it due to <u>random error</u>. This means that <u>each result</u> has some <u>uncertainty</u> to it.

2) The measurements you make will also have some uncertainty in them due to <u>limits</u> in the <u>resolution</u> of the equipment you use (see page 6).

3) This all means that the <u>mean</u> of a set of results will also have some uncertainty to it. You can calculate the uncertainty of a <u>mean result</u> using the equation:

4) The <u>larger</u> the range, the <u>less precise</u> your results are and the <u>more uncertainty</u> there will be in your results. Uncertainties are shown using the '±' symbol.

The range is the largest value minus the smallest value.

$$\text{uncertainty} = \frac{\text{range}}{2}$$

EXAMPLE: The table below shows the results of an experiment to determine the resistance of a piece of wire in a circuit. Calculate the uncertainty of the mean.

Repeat	1	2	3	mean
Resistance (Ω)	4.20	3.80	3.70	3.90

1) First work out the range:
Range = 4.20 − 3.70
= 0.5 Ω

2) Use the range to find the uncertainty:
Uncertainty = range ÷ 2 = 0.5 ÷ 2 = 0.25 Ω   So, uncertainty of the mean = 3.90 ± 0.25 Ω

5) Measuring a <u>greater amount</u> of something helps to <u>reduce uncertainty</u>. For example, in a speed experiment, measuring the distance travelled over a <u>longer period</u> compared to a shorter period will <u>reduce</u> the <u>percentage uncertainty</u> in your results.

Evaluations — Describe How it Could be Improved

An evaluation is a <u>critical analysis</u> of the whole investigation.

1) You should comment on the <u>method</u> — was it <u>valid</u>? Did you control all the other variables to make it a <u>fair test</u>?

2) Comment on the <u>quality</u> of the <u>results</u> — was there <u>enough evidence</u> to reach a valid <u>conclusion</u>? Were the results <u>repeatable</u>, <u>reproducible</u>, <u>accurate</u> and <u>precise</u>?

3) Were there any <u>anomalous</u> results? If there were <u>none</u> then <u>say so</u>. If there were any, try to <u>explain</u> them — were they caused by <u>errors</u> in measurement? Were there any other <u>variables</u> that could have <u>affected</u> the results? You should comment on the level of <u>uncertainty</u> in your results too.

4) All this analysis will allow you to say how <u>confident</u> you are that your conclusion is <u>right</u>.

5) Then you can suggest any <u>changes</u> to the <u>method</u> that would <u>improve</u> the quality of the results, so that you could have <u>more confidence</u> in your conclusion. For example, you might suggest <u>changing</u> the way you controlled a variable, or <u>increasing</u> the number of <u>measurements</u> you took. Taking more measurements at <u>narrower intervals</u> could give you a <u>more accurate result</u>. For example:

<u>Springs</u> have an <u>elastic limit</u> (a maximum extension before they stop springing back to their original size). Say you use several <u>identical</u> springs to do an experiment to find the elastic limit of the springs. If you apply forces of 1 N, 2 N, 3 N, 4 N and 5 N, and from the results see that the elastic limit is somewhere <u>between 4 N and 5 N</u>, you could then <u>repeat</u> the experiment with one of the other springs, taking <u>more measurements between 4 N and 5 N</u> to get a <u>more accurate</u> value for the elastic limit.

6) You could also make more <u>predictions</u> based on your conclusion. Then <u>further experiments</u> could be carried out to test them.

When suggesting improvements to the investigation, always make sure that you say why you think this would make the results better.

Evaluation — next time, I'll make sure I don't burn the lab down...

So there you have it — Working Scientifically. Make sure you know this stuff like the back of your hand. It's not just in the lab that you'll need to know how to work scientifically. You can be asked about it in the exams as well.

Distance, Displacement, Speed and Velocity

To understand the difference between <u>distance</u> and <u>displacement</u>, or <u>speed</u> and <u>velocity</u>, you've got to know the difference between a <u>scalar</u> quantity and a <u>vector</u> quantity. Then you can race through this page.

Vectors *Have Magnitude and Direction*

1) Vector quantities have a <u>magnitude</u> (size) and a <u>direction</u>.

2) Lots of <u>physical quantities</u> are vector quantities:

> <u>Vector quantities</u>: force, velocity, displacement, weight, acceleration, momentum, etc.

3) Some physical quantities <u>only</u> have magnitude and <u>no direction</u>. These are called <u>scalar quantities</u>:

> <u>Scalar quantities</u>: speed, distance, mass, energy, temperature, time, etc.

> <u>Velocity</u> is a <u>vector</u>, but <u>speed</u> is a <u>scalar</u> quantity.
> Both bikes are travelling at the same <u>speed</u>, *v*.
> They have <u>different velocities</u> because
> they are travelling in different <u>directions</u>.

Distance *is Scalar, Displacement is a Vector*

1) <u>Distance</u> is just <u>how far</u> an object has moved. It's a <u>scalar</u> quantity so it doesn't involve <u>direction</u>.

2) Displacement is a <u>vector</u> quantity. It measures the distance and direction in a <u>straight line</u> from an object's <u>starting point</u> to its <u>finishing point</u> — e.g. the plane flew 5 metres <u>north</u>. The direction could be <u>relative to a point</u>, e.g. <u>towards the school</u>, or a <u>bearing</u> (a <u>three-digit angle from north</u>, e.g. 035°).

3) If you walk 5 m <u>north</u>, then 5 m <u>south</u>, your <u>displacement</u> is <u>0 m</u> but the <u>distance</u> travelled is <u>10 m</u>.

Speed *and Velocity are Both How Fast You're Going*

1) <u>Speed and velocity</u> both measure <u>how fast</u> you're going, but <u>speed</u> is a <u>scalar</u> and <u>velocity</u> is a <u>vector</u>:

> <u>Speed</u> is just <u>how fast</u> you're going (e.g. 30 mph or 20 m/s) with no regard to the direction.
> <u>Velocity</u> is speed in a given <u>direction</u>, e.g. 30 mph north or 20 m/s, 060°.

2) This means you can have objects travelling at a <u>constant speed</u> with a <u>changing velocity</u>. This happens when the object is <u>changing direction</u> whilst staying at the <u>same speed</u>.

3) For an object travelling at a <u>constant</u> speed, <u>distance</u>, (average) <u>speed</u> and <u>time</u> are related by the formula:

> distance travelled (m) = (average) speed (m/s) × time (s)

4) Objects <u>rarely</u> travel at a <u>constant speed</u>. E.g. when you <u>walk</u>, <u>run</u> or travel in a <u>car</u>, your speed is <u>always changing</u>. Make sure you have an idea of the <u>typical speeds</u> for different transport methods:

1) <u>Walking</u> — <u>1.4 m/s</u> (5 km/h)
2) <u>Running</u> — <u>3 m/s</u> (11 km/h)
3) <u>Cycling</u> — <u>5.5 m/s</u> (20 km/h)
4) <u>Cars</u> in a <u>built-up area</u> — <u>13 m/s</u> (47 km/h)
5) <u>Aeroplanes</u> — <u>250 m/s</u> (900 km/h)

6) <u>Cars</u> on a <u>motorway</u> — <u>31 m/s</u> (112 km/h)
7) <u>Trains</u> — up to <u>55 m/s</u> (200 km/h)
8) <u>Wind</u> speed — <u>5 – 20 m/s</u>
9) Speed of <u>sound</u> in <u>air</u> — <u>340 m/s</u>
10) <u>Ferries</u> — 15 m/s (54 km/h)

My life's feeling pretty scalar — I've no idea where I'm headed...

This all seems pretty basic, but it's vital you understand it if you want to make it through the rest of this topic.

Q1   Name two examples of: a) a scalar quantity   b) a vector quantity   [4 marks]

Q2   A sprinter runs 200 m in 25 s. Calculate his average speed.   [2 marks]

Acceleration

Uniform acceleration sounds fancy, but it's just <u>speeding up</u> (or <u>slowing down</u>) at a <u>constant rate</u>.

Acceleration is How Quickly You're Speeding Up

1) Acceleration is definitely <u>not</u> the same as <u>velocity</u> or <u>speed</u>.

2) Acceleration is the <u>change in velocity</u> in a certain amount of <u>time</u>.

3) You can find the average acceleration of an object using:

Change in velocity (m/s) where u is the initial velocity in m/s and v is the final velocity in m/s

Acceleration (m/s²)

$$a = \frac{(v - u)}{t}$$

Time (s)

Initial velocity is just the starting velocity of the object.

4) <u>Deceleration</u> is just <u>negative</u> acceleration (if something <u>slows down</u>, the change in velocity is <u>negative</u>).

You Need to be Able to Estimate Accelerations

You might have to <u>estimate</u> the <u>acceleration</u> (or <u>deceleration</u>) of an object:

EXAMPLE: A car is travelling at 15 m/s, when it collides with a tree and comes to a stop. Estimate the deceleration of the car.

1) <u>Estimate</u> how long it would take the car to <u>stop</u>.

2) Put these numbers into the <u>acceleration equation</u>.

3) As the car has slowed down, the <u>change in velocity</u> and so the acceleration is <u>negative</u> — the car is <u>decelerating</u>.

The car comes to a stop in ~1 s.

$a = (v - u) \div t$
$ = (0 - 15) \div 1$
$ = -15$ m/s²

The ~ symbol just means it's an approximate value (or answer).

So the deceleration is about 15 m/s²

From the deceleration, you can estimate the <u>forces</u> involved too — more about that on page 16.

Uniform Acceleration Means a Constant Acceleration

1) <u>Constant acceleration</u> is sometimes called <u>uniform acceleration</u>.

2) Acceleration <u>due to gravity</u> (g) is <u>uniform</u> for objects in free fall. It's roughly equal to <u>10 m/s²</u> near the Earth's surface and has the same value as gravitational field strength (p.17).

3) You can use this <u>equation</u> for <u>uniform</u> acceleration:

Final velocity (m/s)

Acceleration (m/s²)

$$v^2 - u^2 = 2 \times a \times x$$

Distance (m)

Initial velocity (m/s)

EXAMPLE: A van travelling at 23 m/s starts decelerating uniformly at 2.0 m/s² as it heads towards a built-up area 112 m away. What will its speed be when it reaches the built-up area?

1) First, <u>rearrange</u> the equation so v^2 is on one side.

2) Now put the <u>numbers</u> in — remember a is <u>negative</u> because it's a deceleration.

3) Finally, <u>square root</u> the whole thing.

$v^2 = u^2 + (2 \times a \times x)$
$v^2 = 23^2 + (2 \times -2.0 \times 112)$
$ = 81$
$v = \sqrt{81} = 9$ m/s

Uniform problems — get a clip-on tie or use the equation above...

You might not be told what equation to use in the exam, so make sure you can spot when to use the equation for uniform acceleration. Make a list of the information you're given to help you see what to do.

Q1 A ball is dropped from a height, h, above the ground. The speed of the ball just before it hits the ground is 5 m/s. Calculate the height the ball is dropped from. (acceleration due to gravity $\approx$ 10 m/s²)   [2 marks]

Distance/Time Graphs

A <u>graph</u> speaks a thousand words, so it's much better than writing 'An object starts from rest and moves at a steady speed of 10 m/s for 2 s until it has reaches a distance of 20 m, then remains stationary for 5 s before increasing its velocity with a constant acceleration for 2.5 s.'

Distance/Time Graphs Tell You How Far Something has Travelled

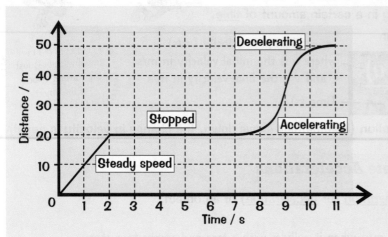

The different parts of a distance/time graph describe the <u>motion</u> of an object:

- The <u>gradient</u> (slope) at <u>any</u> point gives the <u>speed</u> of the object.
- <u>Flat</u> sections are where it's <u>stopped</u>.
- A <u>steeper</u> graph means it's going <u>faster</u>.
- <u>Curves</u> represent <u>acceleration</u>.
- A <u>curve getting steeper</u> means it's <u>speeding up</u> (increasing gradient).
- A <u>levelling off</u> curve means it's <u>slowing down</u> (decreasing gradient).

The Speed of an Object can be Found From a Distance/Time Graph

You can find the <u>speed</u> at any time on a distance/time graph:

1) If the graph is a <u>straight line</u>, the speed at any point along that line is equal to the <u>gradient</u> of the line.

> For example, in the graph above, the speed at any time between 0 s and 2 s is:
>
> $$\text{Speed} = \text{gradient} = \frac{\text{change in the vertical}}{\text{change in the horizontal}} = \frac{20}{2} = \underline{10 \text{ m/s}}$$

2) If the graph is <u>curved</u>, to find the speed at a certain time you need to draw a <u>tangent</u> to the curve at that point, and then find the <u>gradient</u> of the <u>tangent</u>.

A tangent is a line that is parallel to the curve at that point.

3) You can also calculate the <u>average speed</u> of an object when it has <u>non-uniform motion</u> (i.e. it's <u>accelerating</u>) by dividing the <u>total distance travelled</u> by the <u>time it takes</u> to travel that distance.

EXAMPLE: The graph shows the distance/time graph for a cyclist on his bike. Calculate:
a) the speed of the bike 25 s into the journey.
b) the average speed of the cyclist from 0 to 30 s.

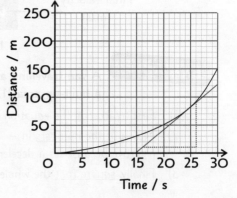

a) Draw the <u>tangent</u> to the curve at 25 s (red line). Then calculate the <u>gradient</u> of the tangent (blue lines).

$$\text{gradient} = \frac{\text{change in the vertical}}{\text{change in the horizontal}} = \frac{80}{10} = 8 \text{ m/s}$$

b) Use the <u>formula</u> from page 12 to find the <u>average speed</u> of the bike.

average speed = distance ÷ time = 150 ÷ 30 = 5 m/s

Tangent — a man who's just come back from holiday...

For practice, try sketching distance/time graphs for different scenarios. Like walking home or running from a bear.

Q1   Sketch a distance/time graph for an object that initially accelerates, then travels at a constant speed, then decelerates to a stop.

[2 marks]

Section 1 — Motion, Forces and Conservation of Energy

Velocity/Time Graphs

Huzzah, more graphs — velocity/time graphs this time. These look a lot like the distance/time graphs on page 14, so make sure you check the labels on the axes really carefully. You don't want to mix them up.

Velocity/Time Graphs can have a Positive or Negative Gradient

How an object's velocity changes over time can be plotted on a velocity/time (or *v/t*) graph.

1) Gradient = acceleration, since acceleration = change in velocity ÷ time.
2) Flat sections represent a steady speed.
3) The steeper the graph, the greater the acceleration or deceleration.
4) Uphill sections (/) are acceleration.
5) Downhill sections (\) are deceleration.
6) A curve means changing acceleration.

If the graph is curved, you can use a tangent to the curve (p.14) at a point to find the acceleration at that point.

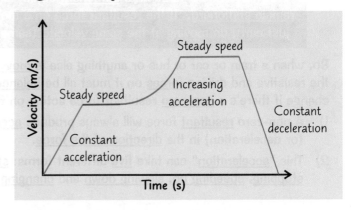

The Distance Travelled is the Area Under the Graph

1) The area under any section of the graph (or all of it) is equal to the distance travelled in that time interval.
2) For bits of the graph where the acceleration's constant, you can split the area into rectangles and triangles to work it out.
3) You can also find the area under the graph by counting the squares under the line and multiplying the number by the value of one square.

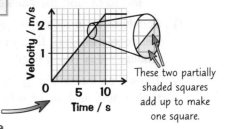

These two partially shaded squares add up to make one square.

EXAMPLE:

The velocity/time graph of a car's journey is plotted.
a) Calculate the acceleration of the car over the first 10 s.
b) How far does the car travel in the first 15 s of the journey?

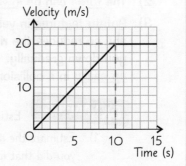

a) This is just the gradient of the line:
$$a = (v - u) \div t$$
$$= (20 - 0) \div 10 = 2 \text{ m/s}^2$$

b) Split the area into a triangle and a rectangle, then add together their areas — remember the area of a triangle is ½ × base × height.

Area = (½ × 10 × 20) + (5 × 20)
= 200 m

Or find the value of one square, count the total number of squares under the line, and then multiply these two values together.

1 square = 2 m/s × 1 s = 2 m
Area = 100 squares
= 100 × 2 = 200 m

Understanding motion graphs — it can be a real uphill struggle...

Make sure you know the differences between distance/time and velocity/time graphs, and how to interpret them.

Q1 A stationary car starts accelerating increasingly for 10 s until it reaches a speed of 20 m/s.
It travels at this speed for 20 s until the driver sees a hazard and brakes.
He decelerates uniformly, coming to a stop 4 s after braking.
a) Draw the velocity/time graph for this journey. [3 marks]
b) Using the graph, calculate the deceleration of the car when it brakes. [2 marks]

Newton's First and Second Laws

In the 1660s, a chap called <u>Isaac Newton</u> worked out his dead useful <u>Laws of Motion</u>. Here are the first <u>two</u>.

A Force is Needed to Change Motion

This may seem simple, but it's important. <u>Newton's First Law</u> says that a resultant force (p.67) is needed to make something <u>start moving</u>, <u>speed up</u> or <u>slow down</u>:

> If the resultant force on a <u>stationary</u> object is <u>zero</u>, the object will <u>remain stationary</u>. If the <u>resultant force</u> on a moving object is <u>zero</u>, it'll just carry on moving at the <u>same velocity</u> (same speed <u>and</u> direction).

So, when a train or car or bus or anything else is <u>moving</u> at a <u>constant velocity</u>, the resistive and driving <u>forces</u> on it must all be <u>balanced</u>. The velocity will only change if there's a <u>non-zero</u> resultant force acting on the object.

1) A non-zero <u>resultant</u> force will always produce <u>acceleration</u> (or deceleration) in the <u>direction of the force</u>.

2) This "<u>acceleration</u>" can take <u>five</u> different forms: <u>starting</u>, <u>stopping</u>, <u>speeding up</u>, <u>slowing down</u> and <u>changing direction</u>.

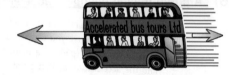

Acceleration is Proportional to the Resultant Force

1) The <u>larger</u> the <u>resultant force</u> acting on an object, the <u>more</u> the object accelerates — the force and the acceleration are <u>directly proportional</u>. You can write this as $F \propto a$.

2) Acceleration is also <u>inversely proportional</u> to the <u>mass</u> of the object — so an object with a <u>larger</u> mass will accelerate <u>less</u> than one with a smaller mass (for a <u>fixed resultant force</u>).

3) There's an incredibly <u>useful formula</u> that describes <u>Newton's Second Law</u>:

Resultant force (N)   Mass (kg)

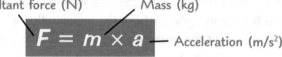

$$F = m \times a$$ — Acceleration (m/s²)

Large Decelerations can be Dangerous

1) <u>Large decelerations</u> of objects and people (e.g. in car crashes) can cause <u>serious injuries</u>. This is because a large deceleration requires a <u>large force</u> — $F = m \times a$.

2) The <u>force</u> can be <u>lowered</u> by <u>slowing</u> the object down over a <u>longer time</u>, i.e. decreasing its deceleration.

3) <u>Safety features</u> in vehicles are designed to <u>increase collision times</u>, which <u>reduces</u> the <u>force</u>, and so reduces the risk of injury. For example, <u>seat belts stretch</u> slightly and <u>air bags</u> slow you down gradually. <u>Crumple zones</u> are areas at the front and back of a vehicle which <u>crumple up easily</u> in a collision, increasing the time taken to stop.

> **EXAMPLE:** Estimate the resultant force acting on a car stopping quickly from 15 m/s.
>
> 1) Estimate the <u>deceleration</u> of the car — you did that for this example on page 13.
>   The car comes to a stop in ~1 s.
> $a = (v - u) \div t = (0 - 15) \div 1 = -15$ m/s²
>
> 2) <u>Estimate</u> the <u>mass</u> of the car.
>   Mass of a car is ~1000 kg.
>
> 3) Put these numbers into <u>Newton's 2nd Law</u>.
> $F = m \times a$
> $= 1000 \times -15 = -15\ 000$ N
>
> The force here is negative as it acts in the opposite direction to the motion of the car.

4) The brakes of a vehicle <u>do work</u> on its wheels (see p.66). This <u>transfers energy</u> from the vehicle's <u>kinetic energy store</u> to the <u>thermal energy store</u> of the <u>brakes</u>. Very large decelerations may cause the brakes to <u>overheat</u> (so they don't work as well). They could also cause the vehicle to <u>skid</u>.

Accelerate your learning — force yourself to revise...

Newton's First Law means that an object moving at a steady speed doesn't need a net force to keep moving.

Q1   Find the resultant force needed to accelerate an 80 kg man on a 10 kg bike at 0.25 m/s². [2 marks]

Weight and Circular Motion

Now for something a bit more _attractive_ — the force of _gravity_. Enjoy...

Weight and Mass are Not the Same

1) <u>Mass</u> is just the <u>amount of 'stuff'</u> in an object. For any given object this will have the same value <u>anywhere</u> in the universe.

2) Mass is a <u>scalar</u> quantity. It's measured in <u>kilograms</u> with a <u>mass</u> balance (an old-fashioned pair of balancing scales).

3) <u>Weight</u> is the <u>force</u> acting on an object due to <u>gravity</u> (the <u>pull</u> of the <u>gravitational force</u> on the object). Close to Earth, this <u>force</u> is caused by the <u>gravitational field</u> around the Earth.

4) Weight is a <u>force</u> measured in <u>newtons</u>. You can think of the force as acting from a <u>single point</u> on the object, called its <u>centre of mass</u> (a point at which you assume the <u>whole</u> mass is concentrated).

5) Weight is measured using a calibrated <u>spring</u> balance (or <u>newton meter</u>).

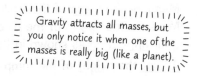
Gravity attracts all masses, but you only notice it when one of the masses is really big (like a planet).

Weight Depends on Mass and Gravitational Field Strength

1) You can calculate the <u>weight</u> of an object if you know its <u>mass</u> (m) and the <u>strength</u> of the <u>gravitational field</u> that it is in (g):

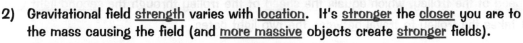
Weight (N) = mass (kg) × gravitational field strength (N/kg)

2) Gravitational field <u>strength</u> varies with <u>location</u>. It's <u>stronger</u> the <u>closer</u> you are to the mass causing the field (and <u>more massive</u> objects create <u>stronger</u> fields).

3) This means that the weight of an object <u>changes</u> with its location.

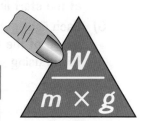

EXAMPLE: What is the weight, in newtons, of a 2.0 kg chicken on Earth (g = 10 N/kg)?

Calculate the weight on <u>Earth</u> using the equation for <u>weight</u> given above.

$W = m \times g = 2.0 \times 10 = 20$ N

The chicken has a weight of 16 N on a mystery planet. What is the gravitational field strength of the planet?

1) <u>Rearrange</u> the weight equation for g.　　$g = W \div m$
2) <u>Substitute</u> the values in.　　$= 16 \div 2.0 = 8.0$ N/kg

Remember — the mass of the chicken is the same on every planet, it's the weight of the chicken that changes.

Circular Motion — Velocity is Constantly Changing

See p.59 for more on gravity causing circular motion.

1) Velocity is both the <u>speed</u> and <u>direction</u> of an object (p.12).

2) If an object is travelling in a circle (at a <u>constant speed</u>) it is <u>constantly changing direction</u>, so it is constantly <u>changing velocity</u>. This means it's <u>accelerating</u>.

3) This means there <u>must</u> be a <u>resultant force</u> (p.67) acting on it.

4) This force acts towards the centre of the circle.

5) This force that keeps something moving in a circle is called a <u>centripetal force</u>.

It's pronounced sen-tree-pee-tal.

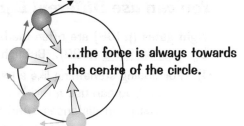
The velocity's in this direction, but...
...the force is always towards the centre of the circle.

I don't think you understand the gravity of this situation...

Remember that weight is a force due to gravity and that it changes depending on the strength of the gravitational field the object is in. Gravity can cause circular motion (in things like moons and satellites — see page 59).

Q1　Calculate the weight in newtons of a 25 kg mass:
　　a) on Earth ($g \approx$ 10 N/kg)　　　b) on the Moon ($g \approx$ 1.6 N/kg)　　　[4 marks]

Investigating Motion

Doing an experiment for yourself can really help you to understand what's going on with $F = ma$ (p.16).

You can Investigate the Motion of a Trolley on a Ramp

1) Measure the mass of the trolley, the unit masses and the hanging hook.
   Measure the length of the piece of card which will interrupt the light gate beams. Then set up
   your apparatus as shown in the diagram below, but don't attach the string to the trolley.

2) Adjust the height of the ramp until the trolley just starts to move.

3) Mark a line on the ramp just before the
   first light gate — this is to make sure the
   trolley travels the same distance every
   time. The light gate will record the initial
   speed of the trolley as it begins to move.

4) Attach the trolley to the hanging mass
   by the string. Hold the trolley still
   at the start line, and then let go of it so that it starts to roll down the slope.

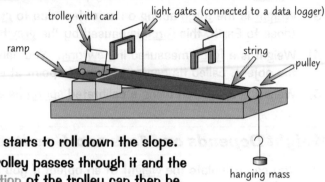

trolley with card

light gates (connected to a data logger)

ramp

string

pulley

hanging mass
on hook

5) Each light gate will record the time when the trolley passes through it and the
   speed of the trolley at that time. The acceleration of the trolley can then be
   found using acceleration = change in speed ÷ time, with the following values:

   • the initial speed of the trolley as it passes through the first light gate (it'll be roughly 0 m/s),
   • the final speed of the trolley, which equals the speed of the trolley through the second light gate,
   • the time it takes the trolley to travel between the two light gates.

By changing the height of the ramp so that the trolley just begins to move, it means that
any other forces that are applied (like the force due to gravity caused by the hanging mass)
will be the main cause of the trolley accelerating as it travels down the ramp (page 16).
The size of this acceleration depends on the mass of the trolley and the size of the accelerating force.

• To investigate the effect of the trolley's mass: add masses one at a time to the trolley. Keep the
  mass on the hook constant (so the accelerating force is constant — where the force is equal to the
  mass on hook × acceleration due to gravity). Repeat steps 2-5 of the experiment above each time.

• To investigate the effect of the accelerating force: start with all the masses loaded onto the trolley and
  transfer the masses to the hook one at a time. Again, repeat steps 2-5 each time you move a mass.

  You transfer the masses because you need to keep the mass of the whole system (the mass of the trolley + the mass on the hook) the same.
  This is because the accelerating force causes BOTH the trolley and the hanging masses to accelerate.

You should find that as the accelerating force increases, the acceleration increases (for a given
trolley mass). So force and acceleration are proportional. As the mass of the trolley increases
its acceleration decreases (for a given force) — mass and acceleration are inversely proportional.

You can use Different Equipment to Measure Distance and Time

Light gates (p.106) are often the best option for short time intervals. They get rid of the human error caused
by reaction times (p.22). But light gates aren't the only way to find the speed of an object:

1) For finding something like a person's walking speed, the distances and times you'll look at are quite
   large. You can use a rolling tape measure (one of those clicky wheel things) and markers to measure
   and mark out distances. And for any times longer than five seconds, you can use a regular stopwatch.

2) If you're feeling a bit high-tech, you could also record a video of the moving object and look at how far
   it travels each frame. If you know how many frames per second the camera records, you can find the
   distance travelled by the object in a given number of frames and the time that it takes to do so.

My acceleration increases with nearby cake...

Make sure you know multiple methods for measuring the speed (distance travelled in a time) of an object.

Q1   Why is it better to use a light gate instead of a stopwatch to measure short time intervals?   [1 mark]

Inertia and Newton's Third Law

Inertia and Newton's Third Law can seem simple on the surface, but they can quickly get confusing.
Make sure you really understand what's going on with them — especially if an object is in equilibrium.

Inertia *is the Tendency for Motion to Remain Unchanged*

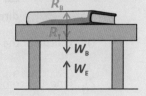

1) Until acted on by a resultant force, objects at rest stay at rest and
objects moving at a constant velocity will stay moving at that velocity (Newton's First Law).

2) This tendency to keep moving with the same velocity is called inertia.

3) An object's inertial mass measures how difficult it is to change the velocity of an object.

4) Inertial mass can be found using Newton's Second Law of $F = ma$ (p.16).
Rearranging this gives $m = F \div a$, so inertial mass is just the ratio of force over acceleration.

Newton's Third Law: Reaction Forces **are Equal** *and* **Opposite**

Newton's Third Law says:

> When two objects interact, the forces they
> exert on each other are equal and opposite.

1) If you push something, say a shopping trolley, the trolley will push back against you, just as hard.

2) And as soon as you stop pushing, so does the trolley. Kinda clever really.

3) So far, so good. The slightly tricky thing to get your head round is this
— if the forces are always equal, how does anything ever go anywhere?
The important thing to remember is that the two forces are acting on different objects.

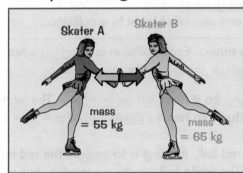

When skater A pushes on skater B (the 'action' force), she feels
an equal and opposite force from skater B's hand (the 'normal
contact' force). Both skaters feel the same sized force, in
opposite directions, and so accelerate away from each other.

Skater A will be accelerated more than skater B, though,
because she has a smaller mass — remember $a = F \div m$.

These equally-sized forces in opposite directions also explain
the principle of conservation of momentum (see pages 20-21).

4) It's a bit more complicated for an object in equilibrium (p.68).
Imagine a book sat on a table:

The weight of the book pulls it down, and the normal reaction force from the table pushes it up.
These forces are equal to each other — the book is in equilibrium and doesn't move.
This is NOT Newton's third law. These forces are different types and they're both acting on the book.

The pairs of forces due to Newton's third law in this case are:

• The book is pulled down by its weight due to gravity from Earth (W_B)
and the book also pulls back up on the Earth (W_E).

• The normal contact force from the table pushing up on the book (R_B) and
the normal contact force from the book pushing down on the table (R_T).

I have a reaction to forces — they bring me out in a rash...

Newton's 3rd law really trips people up, so make sure you understand exactly what objects the forces are acting on
and how that results in movement (or lack of it). Then have a crack at this question to practise what you know.

Q1   A full shopping trolley and an empty one are moving at the same speed. Explain why it is
easier to stop the empty trolley than the full trolley over the same amount of time.   [1 mark]

Momentum

A large rugby player running very fast has much more momentum than a skinny one out for a Sunday afternoon stroll. It's something that all moving objects have, so you better get your head around it.

Momentum = Mass × Velocity

Momentum is a property that all moving objects have. (Think of it as how much 'oomph' something has.) It's defined as the product of the object's mass and velocity:

$$p = m \times v$$ momentum (kg m/s) = mass (kg) × velocity (m/s)

1) The greater the mass of an object, or the greater its velocity, the more momentum the object has.
2) Momentum is a vector quantity — it has size and direction.

EXAMPLE:

A 50 kg cheetah is running at 60 m/s. Calculate its momentum.

$p = m \times v = 50 \times 60$
$= 3000$ kg m/s

EXAMPLE:

A boy has a mass of 30 kg and a momentum of 75 kg m/s. Calculate his velocity.

$v = p \div m = 75 \div 30 = 2.5$ m/s

Total Momentum Before = Total Momentum After

A closed system is just a fancy way of saying that no external forces act.

In a closed system, the total momentum before an event (e.g. a collision) is the same as after the event. This is called conservation of momentum. You can use this to help you calculate things like the velocity or mass of objects in a collision.

In snooker, balls of the same size and mass collide with each other. Each collision is an event where the momentum of each ball changes, but the overall momentum stays the same (momentum is conserved).

Before: (m) →v (m)

The red ball is stationary, so it has zero momentum. The white ball is moving with a velocity v, so has a momentum of $p = m \times v$.

After: (m) → (m) →

The white ball hits the red ball, causing it to move. The red ball now has momentum. The white ball continues moving, but at a much smaller velocity (and so a much smaller momentum).

The combined momentum of the red and white balls is equal to the original momentum of the white ball, m × v.

EXAMPLE:

A 1500 kg car, travelling at 25 m/s, crashes into the back of a parked car. The parked car has a mass of 1000 kg. The two cars lock together and continue moving in the same direction as the original moving car. Calculate the velocity that the two cars move with.

1) Calculate the momentum before the collision.

$p = m \times v = 1500 \times 25 = 37\ 500$ kg m/s

Total momentum before = total momentum after

2) Find the combined mass of the cars.

New mass of joined cars = 2500 kg = M

3) Rearrange the equation to find the velocity of the cars.

$v = p \div M = 37\ 500 \div 2500 = 15$ m/s

Learn this stuff — it'll only take a moment... um...

Conservation of momentum is incredibly handy — there's more on using it on the next page.

Q1 Calculate the momentum of a 60 kg woman running at 3 m/s. [2 marks]

Q2 Describe how momentum is conserved by a gun recoiling (moving backwards) as it shoots a bullet. [4 marks]

Changes in Momentum

A <u>force</u> causes the <u>momentum</u> of an object to <u>change</u>. A <u>bigger force</u> makes it change <u>faster</u>.

Forces Cause Changes in Momentum

1) When a resultant <u>force</u> acts on an object for a certain amount of time, it causes a <u>change in momentum</u>. <u>Newton's 2nd Law</u> can explain this:

   - A <u>resultant force</u> on an object causes it to <u>accelerate</u>: force = mass × acceleration (see p.16).

   - <u>Acceleration</u> is just <u>change in velocity</u> over <u>time</u>, so: force $= \dfrac{\text{mass} \times \text{change in velocity}}{\text{time}}$.
   This means a force applied to an object over any time interval will change the object's <u>velocity</u>.

   - <u>Mass × change in velocity</u> is equal to <u>change in momentum</u>, so you end up with the equation:

$$\text{force (N)} = \frac{\text{change in momentum (kg m/s)}}{\text{time (s)}} \quad \text{or} \quad F = \frac{(mv - mu)}{t}$$

2) The <u>faster</u> a given change in momentum happens, the <u>bigger the force</u> causing the change must be (i.e. if t gets <u>smaller</u> in the equation above, F gets <u>bigger</u>).

3) So if someone's momentum changes <u>very quickly</u>, like in a <u>car crash</u>, the <u>forces</u> on the body will be very <u>large</u>, and more likely to cause <u>injury</u>. There's more about this on p.16.

4) You can also think of changes in momentum in collisions in terms of <u>acceleration</u> — a change in momentum normally involves a <u>change in velocity</u>, which is what acceleration is (see p.13).

5) As you know, $F = ma$, so the <u>larger the acceleration</u> (or deceleration), the <u>larger the force</u> needed to produce it.

Conservation of Momentum Shows Newton's Third Law

The equation above can help to show <u>Newton's Third Law</u> (<u>reaction</u> forces are <u>equal</u> and <u>opposite</u>). Take the <u>snooker balls</u> from the previous page.

1) <u>Before</u> the collision, the <u>white</u> ball has a momentum of 0.15 × 4 = 0.6 kg m/s. The <u>red</u> ball has a momentum of <u>zero</u>.

2) The <u>total momentum</u> of the system is 0.6 kg m/s.

3) When the balls collide, the <u>white</u> ball exerts a <u>force</u> on the <u>red</u> ball. This force causes the <u>red ball</u> to <u>start moving</u>.

4) Due to <u>Newton's 3rd Law</u>, the <u>red</u> ball also exerts an <u>equal</u> but <u>opposite</u> force on the <u>white</u> ball. This force causes the <u>white</u> ball to <u>slow down</u>.

5) The collision lasts <u>0.1 s</u>. <u>After</u> the collision, the white ball <u>continues moving</u> at 1 m/s. The red ball <u>begins moving</u> at 3 m/s.

6) The total momentum is (0.15 × 1) + (0.15 × 3) = 0.6 kg m/s. Momentum is <u>conserved</u>.

7) You can <u>calculate</u> the size of the <u>force</u> that caused this <u>change of velocity</u> (and so <u>change of momentum</u>) for each ball:

8) The <u>force exerted on the white ball</u> (by the red ball) is <u>equal and opposite</u> to the force exerted <u>on the red ball</u> (by the white ball). This shows <u>Newton's Third Law</u>.

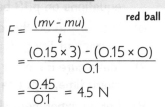

white ball
$$F = \frac{(mv - mu)}{t}$$
$$= \frac{(0.15 \times 1) - (0.15 \times 4)}{0.1}$$
$$= \frac{-0.45}{0.1} = -4.5 \text{ N}$$

red ball
$$F = \frac{(mv - mu)}{t}$$
$$= \frac{(0.15 \times 3) - (0.15 \times 0)}{0.1}$$
$$= \frac{0.45}{0.1} = 4.5 \text{ N}$$

Homework this week — play pool to investigate momentum...

Sigh if only. Momentum is a pretty fundamental bit of physics — learn it well. Then have a go at this question.

Q1 Calculate the force a tennis racket needs to apply to a 58 g tennis ball to accelerate it from rest to 34 m/s in 11.6 ms. [3 marks]

Stopping Distances and Reaction Times

The <u>stopping distance</u> of a vehicle is the distance covered between the driver <u>first spotting</u> a hazard and the vehicle coming to a <u>complete stop</u>. It's made up of the <u>thinking distance</u> and the <u>braking distance</u>.

Stopping Distance = Thinking Distance + Braking Distance

The <u>longer</u> it takes a car to <u>stop</u> after seeing a hazard, the <u>higher</u> the risk of <u>crashing</u>. The distance it takes to stop a car (<u>stopping distance</u>) is divided into the <u>thinking distance</u> and the <u>braking distance</u>:

The <u>thinking distance</u> is the distance the car travels in the driver's <u>reaction time</u> (the time between <u>noticing the hazard</u> and <u>applying the brakes</u>). It's affected by <u>two main factors</u>:
1) Your <u>reaction time</u> — this is increased by <u>tiredness</u>, <u>alcohol</u>, <u>drugs</u> and <u>distractions</u>.
2) Your <u>speed</u> — the <u>faster</u> you're going, the <u>further</u> you'll travel during your reaction time.

The <u>braking distance</u> is the distance taken to stop <u>once the brakes have been applied</u>. It's affected by:
1) Your <u>speed</u> — the <u>faster</u> you're going, the <u>longer</u> it takes to stop (see next page).
2) The <u>mass</u> of the car — a car full of <u>people</u> and <u>luggage</u> won't stop as quickly as an empty car.
3) The condition of the <u>brakes</u> — <u>worn</u> or <u>faulty</u> brakes won't be able to brake with <u>as much force</u>.
4) How much <u>friction</u> is between your <u>tyres</u> and the <u>road</u> — you're more likely to <u>skid</u> if the road is <u>dirty</u>, if it's <u>icy or wet</u> or if the <u>tyres</u> are <u>bald</u> (tyres must have a minimum <u>tread depth</u> of <u>1.6 mm</u>).

In the exam, you may need to <u>spot</u> the <u>factors</u> affecting thinking and braking distance in <u>different situations</u>. E.g. if a parent is driving her <u>children</u> to school <u>early</u> in the morning on an <u>autumn</u> day, her <u>thinking</u> distance could be affected by <u>tiredness</u>, or by her children <u>distracting</u> her. Her <u>braking</u> distance could be affected by <u>ice</u>, or by <u>leaves</u> on the road reducing the <u>friction</u>/<u>grip</u>.

The Ruler Drop Experiment Measures Reaction Times

<u>Everyone's</u> reaction time is different and many different <u>factors</u> affect it (see above).

One way of measuring reaction times is to use a <u>computer-based test</u> (e.g. <u>clicking a mouse</u> when the screen changes colour). Another is the <u>ruler drop test</u>:

1) Sit with your arm <u>resting</u> on the edge of a table (this should stop you moving your arm up or down during the test). Get someone else to hold a ruler so it <u>hangs between</u> your thumb and forefinger, lined up with <u>zero</u>. You may need a <u>third person</u> to be at <u>eye level with the ruler</u> to check it's lined up.

2) Without giving any warning, the person holding the ruler <u>drops it</u>. Close your thumb and finger to try to <u>catch the ruler as quickly as possible</u>.

3) The measurement on the ruler at the point where it was caught is <u>how far</u> the ruler dropped in the time it took you to react.

ruler hanging between thumb and forefinger → finger in line with zero

4) The <u>longer</u> the <u>distance</u>, the <u>longer</u> the <u>reaction time</u>.

5) You can calculate <u>how long</u> the ruler was falling for (the <u>reaction</u> time) using the equations on p.13 because its <u>acceleration</u> is <u>constant</u> (and equal to g, 10 m/s^2).

ruler is dropped without warning

6) It's <u>hard</u> to do this experiment <u>accurately</u>, so do a lot of <u>repeats</u> and take an <u>average</u> of the <u>distance</u> the ruler fell. Use this average in your calculations.

distance fallen

7) Make sure it's a <u>fair test</u> — keep the <u>variables</u> you <u>aren't testing</u> the <u>same</u> every time, e.g. use the <u>same ruler</u> for each repeat and have the <u>same person</u> dropping it.

8) For an experiment like this, a typical reaction time is around <u>0.2-0.6 s</u>.

9) A person's reaction time in a <u>real</u> situation (e.g. when driving) will be <u>longer</u> than that, though. Typically, an <u>alert</u> driver will have a reaction time of about <u>1 s</u>.

Stop right there — and learn this page...

Bad visibility also causes accidents — if it's foggy, it's harder to notice a hazard, so there's less room to stop.

Q1   Drivers on long journeys should take regular breaks. Explain why, in terms of stopping distance. [3 marks]

Stopping Safely

So now you know what affects a car's stopping distance, let's have a look at the facts and figures.

Drivers Need to Leave Enough Space to Stop

1) These typical stopping distances are from the Highway Code.

2) To avoid an accident, drivers must leave enough space in front so they could stop safely — at least equal to the stopping distance for their speed.

3) Speed limits are really important because speed affects stopping distances so much. (Remember, weather and road conditions can affect them too.)

hazard spotted   9 m   14 m
                            Total 23 m
                            6 car lengths
30 mph / 13 m/s

thinking distance   braking distance

                 15 m   38 m
                                   Total 53 m
                                   13 car lengths
50 mph / 22 m/s   21 m   Total 96 m
                                            75 m   24 car lengths
70 mph / 31 m/s

4) As speed increases, thinking distance increases at the same rate. This is because the driver's reaction time stays fairly constant, but the higher the speed, the further you go in that time ($d = st$, p.12).

5) However, braking distance and speed have a squared relationship — if speed doubles, braking distance increases by a factor of 4 (2^2), and if speed trebles, braking distance increases by a factor of 9 (3^2).

The brakes of a car do work on the car's wheels (see page 66). This transfers energy from the car's kinetic energy store to the thermal energy store of the brakes.

To stop a car, the brakes must transfer all of this energy, so:

There's more on these equations on pages 24 and 65.

> **Energy in the car's kinetic energy store = Work done by the brakes**
> $$\tfrac{1}{2} \times m \times v^2 \qquad = \qquad F \times d$$
> mass of the car — speed of car — braking force — braking distance

This means doubling the mass doubles the braking distance.

You can Estimate the Distances Involved in Stopping

EXAMPLE: A car travelling at 25 m/s makes an emergency stop to avoid a hazard. The braking force applied to the car is 5000 N. Estimate the total distance taken to stop.

1) Estimate the driver's reaction time.
2) Calculate the thinking distance.
3) To work out the braking distance, rearrange the equation above for d, and estimate the mass of the car.
4) Add the thinking distance and braking distance to give the stopping distance.

Reaction time is ~1 s.

$d = v \times t = 25 \times 1 = 25$ m

$d = (\tfrac{1}{2} \times m \times v^2) \div F$

Mass of a car is ~1000 kg

$d = (\tfrac{1}{2} \times 1000 \times 25^2) \div 5000$

$= 62.5$ m

$25 + 62.5 = 87.5$ m   **Distance is ~90 m**

Make sure you can estimate the mass of objects. A car's mass is ~1000 kg. A single decker bus is ~10 000 kg and a loaded lorry is ~30 000 kg.

Thinking and Braking Distance can be Seen on v/t Graphs

See p.15 for more on v/t graphs.

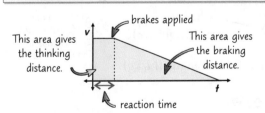

This area gives the thinking distance.
brakes applied
This area gives the braking distance.
reaction time

But if the driver is going faster, and he's a bit tired.....

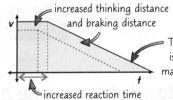

increased thinking distance and braking distance
The gradient (deceleration) is the same though, as the maximum force applied to the brakes hasn't changed.
increased reaction time

It's enough to put you off learning to drive, isn't it...

This is quite a tough page, but it's important, so head back to the top and read it again.

Q1   Estimate the size of the force needed to stop a lorry travelling at 16 m/s within 50 m.   [4 marks]

Energy Stores

Energy stores are <u>different ways</u> of storing energy. Simple really...

Energy is Transferred Between Energy Stores

<u>Energy</u> can be transferred between and held in different <u>energy stores</u>. There are eight you need to know:

1) <u>KINETIC</u>.............................. — anything <u>moving</u> has energy in its <u>kinetic energy store</u> (see below).
2) <u>THERMAL</u>............................ — <u>any object</u> — the <u>hotter</u> it is, the <u>more</u> energy it has in this <u>store</u>.
3) <u>CHEMICAL</u>........................... — anything that can release energy by a <u>chemical reaction</u>, e.g. <u>food</u>, <u>fuels</u>.
4) <u>GRAVITATIONAL POTENTIAL</u>... — anything in a <u>gravitational field</u> (i.e. anything that can <u>fall</u>) (see below).
5) <u>ELASTIC POTENTIAL</u>............. — anything stretched, like <u>springs</u>, <u>rubber bands</u>, etc. (p.100).
6) <u>ELECTROSTATIC</u>.................. — e.g. two <u>charges</u> that attract or repel each other.
7) <u>MAGNETIC</u>.......................... — e.g. two <u>magnets</u> that attract or repel each other.
8) <u>NUCLEAR</u>............................ — <u>atomic nuclei</u> release energy from this store in <u>nuclear reactions</u>.

A Moving Object has Energy in its Kinetic Energy Store

1) When an object is <u>moving</u>, it has <u>energy</u> in its <u>kinetic energy store</u>.
2) Energy is transferred <u>to</u> this store if an object <u>speeds up</u> and <u>away</u> from this store if it <u>slows down</u>.
3) How much energy is in this store depends on both the object's <u>mass</u> and its <u>speed</u>.
4) The <u>greater its mass</u> and the <u>faster it's going</u>, the <u>more</u> energy it has in its kinetic energy store.
5) For example, a <u>high-speed train</u> will have <u>a lot more energy</u> in its kinetic energy store than you running.
6) You can find the energy in a <u>kinetic energy store</u> using:

$$\text{kinetic energy} = 0.5 \times \text{mass} \times (\text{speed})^2$$
$$\text{(J)} \qquad\qquad \text{(kg)} \qquad \text{(m/s)}^2$$

or $KE = \frac{1}{2} \times m \times v^2$

7) If you <u>double the mass</u>, the energy in the kinetic energy store <u>doubles</u>.
   If you <u>double the speed</u>, though, the energy in the kinetic energy store <u>quadruples</u>
   (increases by a factor of <u>4</u>) — it's because of the '(speed)²' in the formula.

EXAMPLE:
A car of mass 1450 kg is travelling at 28 m/s. Calculate the energy in its kinetic energy store, giving your answer to 2 s.f.

kinetic energy = 0.5 × mass × (speed)²
= 0.5 × 1450 × 28² = 568 400 = 570 000 J (to 2 s.f.)

Watch out for the (speed)²
— that's where people tend to
make mistakes and lose marks.

An Object at a Height has Energy in its Gravitational Potential Energy Store

1) When an object is at any <u>height</u> above the Earth's surface, it will have <u>energy</u> in its <u>gravitational potential energy store</u>.
2) You can <u>calculate</u> the <u>change in energy</u> in the gravitational potential energy store using the equation:

Change in gravitational potential energy (J) $\qquad \Delta GPE = m \times g \times \Delta h \qquad$ Change in vertical height (m)

Mass (kg) $\qquad$ Gravitational field strength (N/kg)

Δ just means 'change in'.

There's potential for a joke here somewhere...

Hopefully this page wasn't too hard — just don't forget that squared sign when you're working and remember that the energy in an object's kinetic energy store only changes if its speed is changing. Now have a crack at this...

Q1   A 2 kg object is dropped from a height of 10 m. Calculate the speed of the object
      after it has fallen 5 m, assuming there is no air resistance. $g = 10$ N/kg.
      [5 marks]

Transferring Energy

Now you know about the different energy stores, it's time to find out how energy is transferred between them.

Conservation of Energy Means Energy is Never Created or Destroyed

Energy can be stored, transferred between stores, and dissipated — but it can never be created or destroyed. The total energy of a closed system has no net change.

See the next page for more on dissipation.

A closed system is just a system (a collection of objects) that can be treated completely on its own and where there is no net change in the system's total energy. If you get a question where the energy of a system increases or decreases, then it's not closed. But you can make it into a closed system by increasing the number of things you treat as part of it. E.g. a pan of water heating on a hob isn't a closed system, but the pan, the gas and the oxygen that burn to heat it, and their surroundings are a closed system.

Energy Transfers Show... well... the Transfer of Energy

Energy can be transferred between stores in four main ways:

1) Mechanically — a force acting on an object (and doing work, p.66), e.g. pushing, stretching, squashing.
2) Electrically — a charge doing work (p.72), e.g. charges moving round a circuit.
3) By heating — energy transferred from a hotter object to a colder object, e.g. heating a pan on a hob.
4) By radiation — energy transferred by waves, e.g. energy from the Sun reaching Earth by light.

Make sure you understand what's going on in these examples of energy transfers:

A BALL ROLLING UP A SLOPE:
The ball does work against the gravitational force, so energy is transferred mechanically from the kinetic energy store of the ball to its gravitational potential energy store.

A BAT HITTING A BALL:
The bat has energy in its kinetic energy store. Some of this is transferred mechanically to the ball's kinetic energy store. Some energy is also transferred mechanically to the thermal energy stores of the bat and the ball (and to the surroundings by heating). The rest is carried away by sound.

A ROCK DROPPED FROM A CLIFF:
Assuming there's no air resistance, gravity does work on the rock, so the rock constantly accelerates towards the ground. Energy is transferred mechanically from the rock's gravitational potential energy store to its kinetic energy store.

A CAR SLOWING DOWN (without braking):
Energy in the kinetic energy store of the car is transferred mechanically (due to friction between the tyres and road), and then by heating, to the thermal energy stores of the car and road.

A KETTLE BOILING WATER:
Energy is transferred electrically from the mains to the heating element of the kettle, and then by heating to the thermal energy store of the water.

You can Draw Diagrams to Show Energy Transfers

You may have to use or draw a diagram like this in the exam, so make sure you understand what it's showing.

Diagrams can make it easier to see what's going on when energy is transferred. The diagram below shows the energy transferred when a ball is thrown upwards, taking air resistance into account. The boxes represent stores and the arrows show transfers:

| kinetic energy store of the ball | mechanically — work done against gravity → | gravitational potential energy store of the ball |
| | mechanically — work done against air resistance → | thermal energy store of the ball and the surroundings |

Energy can't be created or destroyed — only talked about a lot...

This is important, so remember it. Energy can only be transferred to a different store, never destroyed.

Q1   Describe the energy transfers that occur when a piece of wood is burning.   [2 marks]

Efficiency

So energy is <u>transferred</u> between different <u>stores</u>. But not all of the energy is transferred to <u>useful</u> stores.

Most Energy Transfers Involve Some Losses, Often by Heating

1) You've already met the <u>principle of conservation of energy</u> on the previous page, but another <u>important principle</u> you need to know is:

> Energy is <u>only useful</u> when it is <u>transferred</u> from one store to a <u>useful store</u>.

2) <u>Useful devices</u> can <u>transfer energy</u> from <u>one store</u> to a <u>useful store</u>.

3) However, some of the <u>input energy</u> is always <u>dissipated or wasted</u>, often to <u>thermal energy stores</u> of the surroundings.

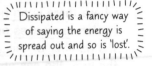
Dissipated is a fancy way of saying the energy is spread out and so is 'lost'.

4) Whenever work is done <u>mechanically</u> (see p.25), <u>frictional forces</u> have to be overcome, including things like <u>moving parts rubbing</u> together, and <u>air resistance</u>. The energy needed to overcome these frictional forces is transferred to the <u>thermal energy stores</u> of whatever's doing the work and the <u>surroundings</u>.

5) This energy usually <u>isn't useful</u>, and is <u>quickly dissipated</u>.

The diagram shows a <u>motor</u> lifting a load.
The motor transfers energy usefully from <u>its</u> <u>kinetic energy store</u> to the <u>kinetic</u> energy store and the <u>gravitational potential</u> energy store of the <u>load</u>, but it also transfers energy <u>mechanically</u> to the <u>thermal energy stores</u> of its moving parts, and <u>electrically</u> to the <u>thermal energy stores</u> of its <u>circuits</u>. This energy is <u>dissipated</u>, heating the surroundings.

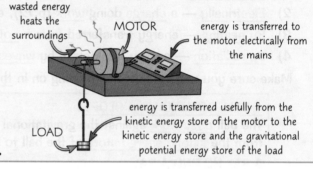

wasted energy heats the surroundings

MOTOR

energy is transferred to the motor electrically from the mains

energy is transferred usefully from the kinetic energy store of the motor to the kinetic energy store and the gravitational potential energy store of the load

LOAD

6) The conservation of energy principle means that:
<u>total energy input = useful energy output + wasted energy</u>.

7) The <u>less energy</u> that's <u>wasted</u>, the <u>more efficient</u> the device is said to be. The amount of energy that's wasted can often be <u>reduced</u> — see next page.

You can Calculate the Efficiency of an Energy Transfer

The <u>efficiency</u> of any device is defined as:

$$\text{efficiency} = \frac{\text{useful energy transferred by device (J)}}{\text{total energy supplied to device (J)}}$$

This will give the efficiency as a decimal. To give it as a percentage, you need to multiply the answer by 100.

EXAMPLE:

A toaster transfers 216 000 J of energy electrically from the mains. 84 000 J of energy is transferred to the bread's thermal energy store. Calculate the efficiency of the toaster.

$$\text{efficiency} = \frac{\text{useful energy transferred by device}}{\text{total energy supplied to device}} = \frac{84\,000}{216\,000} = 0.388... = 0.39 \text{ (to 2 s.f.)}$$

This could also be written as 39% (to 2 s.f.).

All devices have an efficiency, but because some energy is <u>always wasted</u>, the efficiency <u>can never be</u> equal to or higher than <u>1 (or 100%)</u>.

Make sure your revising efficiency is high...

One really important thing to take from here — devices that transfer energy from one store to other stores will always transfer energy to stores that aren't useful. And when I say always, I mean always. <u>Always</u>. (Always.)

Q1 An electrical device wastes 420 J of energy when it has an input energy of 500 J. Calculate the efficiency of the device as a percentage. [3 marks]

Reducing Unwanted Energy Transfers

There are many ways you can <u>reduce</u> the amount of energy that is <u>wasted</u> during a process (and so <u>increase</u> <u>its efficiency</u>) — <u>lubrication</u> and <u>thermal insulation</u> are two of the main ones that you need to know about.

You can Use Diagrams to Show Efficiency

<u>No device</u> is 100% efficient (see previous page), but some are <u>more efficient</u> than others. You can use diagrams like the one below to show the different <u>energy transfers</u> made by a device, and so how <u>efficient</u> it is:

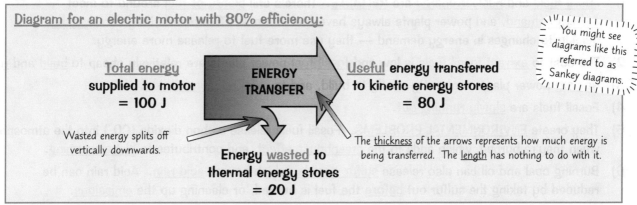

<u>Diagram for an electric motor with 80% efficiency:</u>

<u>Total energy</u>
supplied to motor
= 100 J

ENERGY
TRANSFER

<u>Useful</u> energy transferred
to kinetic energy stores
= 80 J

Wasted energy splits off
vertically downwards.

Energy <u>wasted</u> to
thermal energy stores
= 20 J

The <u>thickness</u> of the arrows represents how much energy is being transferred. The <u>length</u> has nothing to do with it.

You might see diagrams like this referred to as Sankey diagrams.

You can <u>reduce</u> the amount of energy that's <u>wasted</u> in various ways — including by <u>lubrication</u> and by <u>thermal insulation</u>. <u>Decreasing</u> the amount of <u>wasted energy</u> means that a <u>higher proportion</u> of the <u>supplied</u> energy is transferred to <u>useful</u> stores, so the <u>efficiency</u> of the process is <u>increased</u>.

Lubrication Reduces Energy Transferred by Friction

1) Whenever something <u>moves</u>, there's usually at least one <u>frictional force</u> acting against it.

2) This <u>transfers</u> energy <u>mechanically</u> (<u>work</u> is done <u>against</u> friction) to the <u>thermal energy store</u> of the objects involved, which is then <u>dissipated</u> by heating to the surroundings. For example, <u>pushing</u> a <u>box</u> along the <u>ground</u> causes energy to be transferred mechanically to the thermal energy stores of the box and the ground. This energy is then <u>radiated away</u> to the thermal energy store of the surroundings.

3) For objects that are touching each other, <u>lubricants</u> can be used to reduce the friction between the objects' surfaces when they move. Lubricants are usually <u>liquids</u> (like <u>oil</u>), so they can <u>flow</u> easily between objects and <u>coat</u> them.

Insulation Reduces the Rate of Energy Transfer by Heating

1) When one side of an object is <u>heated</u>, the particles in the <u>hotter</u> part <u>vibrate</u> more and <u>collide</u> with each other. This transfers energy from their <u>kinetic energy stores</u> to <u>other particles</u>, which then vibrate faster.

2) This process is called <u>conduction</u>. It <u>transfers energy</u> through the object.

3) All materials have a <u>thermal conductivity</u> — it describes how well a material transfers energy by conduction. For example, <u>metals</u> have a <u>high thermal conductivity</u> and <u>gases</u> (like <u>air</u>) have a <u>low thermal conductivity</u>.

4) In a <u>building</u>, the lower the thermal conductivity of its <u>walls</u>, the slower the rate of energy transfer through them (meaning the building will <u>cool more slowly</u>).

5) Some houses have <u>cavity walls</u>, made up of an inner and an outer wall with an <u>air gap</u> in the middle. The air gap reduces the amount of energy transferred by <u>conduction</u>, because air has a very low thermal conductivity.

6) <u>Thicker</u> walls help too — the thicker the wall, the slower the rate of energy transfer.

Don't waste energy — turn the TV off while you revise...

Unwanted energy transfers can cost you a lot in energy bills — it's why so many people invest in home insulation.

Q1 Suggest one way to improve the efficiency of an electric motor. [1 mark]

Energy Resources

There are lots of energy resources available on Earth. They are either renewable or non-renewable resources.

Non-Renewable Energy Resources *Will Run Out One Day*

Non-renewable energy resources are fossil fuels and nuclear fuel (uranium and plutonium). They currently provide most of the world's energy. Fossil fuels are natural resources that form underground over millions of years that are typically burnt to provide energy. The three main fossil fuels are coal, oil and (natural) gas.

1) Fossil fuels and nuclear energy are RELIABLE. There's still plenty of fuel around to meet current demand, and power plants always have fuel in stock. This means they can respond quickly to changes in energy demand — they use more fuel to release more energy.

2) The cost to extract fossil fuels is low and fossil fuel power plants are relatively cheap to build and run.

3) Nuclear power plants are pretty costly to build, and to safely decommission.

4) Fossil fuels are slowly running out.

5) They create ENVIRONMENTAL PROBLEMS. Fossil fuels release carbon dioxide (CO_2) into the atmosphere when they're burned, which adds to the greenhouse effect, and contributes to global warming.

6) Burning coal and oil can also release sulfur dioxide, which causes acid rain. Acid rain can be reduced by taking the sulfur out before the fuel is burned, or cleaning up the emissions.

7) Oil spillages cause serious environmental problems, affecting mammals and birds that live in and around the sea. We try to avoid them, but they'll always happen.

8) Nuclear power is clean but the nuclear waste is very dangerous and difficult to dispose of. And there's always the risk of a major catastrophe like the Fukushima disaster in Japan.

Renewable Energy Resources *Will Never Run Out*

Renewable energy resources include:
1) Bio-fuels
2) Wind
3) The Sun (solar)
4) Hydro-electricity
5) Tides

- These will never run out — the energy can be 'renewed' as it is used.
- Most of them do damage the environment, but in less nasty ways than non-renewables.
- The trouble is they don't provide much energy and some of them are unreliable because they depend on the weather.

Bio-fuels *are Made from Plants and Waste*

1) Bio-fuels are renewable energy resources created from either plant products or animal dung. They can be solid, liquid or gas and can be burnt to produce electricity or run cars in the same way as fossil fuels.

2) They are supposedly carbon neutral, although there is some debate about this as it's only really true if you keep growing plants (or raising animals) at the rate that you're burning things.

3) Bio-fuels are fairly reliable, as crops take a relatively short time to grow and different crops can be grown all year round. However, they cannot respond to immediate energy demands. To combat this, bio-fuels are continuously produced and stored for when they are needed.

4) The cost to refine bio-fuels is very high and some worry that growing crops specifically for bio-fuels will mean there isn't enough space or water to meet the demands for crops that are grown for food.

5) In some regions, large areas of forest have been cleared to make room to grow bio-fuels, resulting in lots of species losing their natural habitats. The decay or burning of this cleared vegetation also increases methane and CO_2 emissions.

Burning poo... lovely...

Given our electricity-guzzling ways, it's pretty important we find ways to generate electricity without destroying the planet. Burning cow pats may not be the ultimate fix, but it's a start. See the next page for more ways.

Q1   State two renewable energy sources. [2 marks]

More Energy Resources

Renewable energy resources, like wind, solar, hydro-electricity and tides, won't run out. They don't generate as much electricity as non-renewables though — if they did we'd all be using solar-powered toasters by now.

Wind Power — *Lots of Little Wind Turbines*

1) Each wind turbine has a generator inside it — wind rotates the blades, which turn the generator and produce electricity. So there's no pollution.
2) Initial costs are quite high, but running costs are minimal.
3) But lots of them are needed to produce as much power as, for example, a coal power plant. This means they can spoil the view. They can also be noisy, which can be annoying for people living nearby.
4) They only work when it's windy, so you can't always supply electricity, or respond to high demand.

Solar Cells — *Expensive but No Environmental Damage*

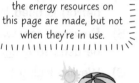

There's some pollution when the energy resources on this page are made, but not when they're in use.

Time to recharge.

1) Solar cells are made from materials that use energy transferred by light to create an electric current.
2) Solar power is often used in remote places where there's not much choice (e.g. the Australian outback) and to power electric road signs and satellites.
3) There's no pollution. (Although they do use quite a lot of energy to make.)
4) Initial costs are high, but there are basically no running costs.
5) They're mainly used to generate electricity on a relatively small scale, e.g. in homes.
6) Solar power is most suitable for sunny countries, but it can be used in cloudy countries like Britain.
7) And of course, you can't make solar power at night or increase production when there's extra demand.

Hydro-electricity — *Building Dams and Flooding Valleys*

1) Producing hydro-electricity usually involves flooding a valley by building a big dam. Rainwater is caught and allowed out through turbines. There is no pollution (as such).
2) There is a big impact on the environment due to the flooding of the valley and possible loss of habitat for some species.
3) A big advantage is it can immediately respond to increased electricity demand — more water can be let out through the turbines to generate more electricity.
4) Initial costs are often high but there are minimal running costs and it's generally a reliable energy source.

Tidal Barrages — *Using the Sun and Moon's Gravity*

None shall pass!

1) Tidal barrages are big dams built across river estuaries with turbines in them.
2) As the tide comes in it fills up the estuary. The water is then let out through turbines at a controlled speed to generate electricity.
3) There is no pollution but they affect boat access, can spoil the view and they alter the habitat for wildlife, e.g. wading birds.
4) Tides are pretty reliable (they always happen twice a day). But the height of the tides is variable and barrages don't work when the water level is the same either side.
5) Initial costs are moderately high, but there are no fuel costs and minimal running costs.

The hydro-electric power you're supplying — it's electrifying...

There are pros and cons to all energy resources. Make sure you know them for solar, wind and water.

Q1   The government is considering closing down a traditional coal-fired power station. Explain the benefits and disadvantages of replacing the power station with a wind farm.   [4 marks]

Trends in Energy Resource Use

Over time, the types of energy resources we use change. There are lots of reasons for this — breakthroughs in technology, understanding more about how they affect the environment or changes in cost are just a few.

Currently We Still Depend on Fossil Fuels

1) Over the 20th century, the electricity use of the UK hugely increased as the population got bigger and people began to use electricity for more and more things.

2) Since the beginning of the 21st century, electricity use in the UK has been decreasing (slowly), as we get better at making appliances more efficient (p.26) and try to be more careful with energy use in our homes.

3) Some of our electricity is produced using fossil fuels and from nuclear power. The rest is generated using renewable energy resources like wind power .

4) Generating electricity isn't the only reason we burn fossil fuels — oil (diesel and petrol) is used to fuel cars, and gas is used to heat homes and cook food.

5) However, renewable energy resources can be used for these purposes as well. Bio-fuels can be used to exclusively power vehicles, and solar water heaters can be used to heat buildings.

6) We are trying to increase our use of renewable energy resources. This move towards renewable energy resources has been triggered by many things...

Energy Resources are Chosen for their Effect on the Environment

1) We now know that burning fossil fuels has a lot of negative effects on the environment (p.28). This has led to many people wanting to use more renewable energy resources that have less of an effect on the environment.

2) Pressure from other countries and the public has meant that governments have begun to introduce targets for using renewable resources. This in turn puts pressure on energy providers to build new power plants that use renewable resources to make sure they do not lose business and money.

3) Car companies have also been affected by this change in attitude towards the environment. Electric cars and hybrids (cars powered by two fuels, e.g. petrol and electricity) are already on the market and their popularity is increasing.

The Use of Renewables is Usually Limited by Reliability and Money

1) Building new renewable power plants costs money, so some smaller energy providers are reluctant to do this — especially when fossil fuels are such a cost effective way of meeting demand.

2) Even if new power plants are built, there are a lot of arguments over where they should be. E.g. many people don't want to live next to a wind farm, which can lead to protests.

3) Some energy resources like wind power are not as reliable as traditional fossil fuels, whilst others cannot increase their power output on demand. This would mean either having to use a combination of different power plants (which would be expensive) or researching ways to improve reliability.

4) Research into improving the reliability and cost of renewable resources takes time and money. This means that, even with funding, it might be years before improvements are made. In the meantime, dependable, non-renewable power stations have to be used.

5) Making personal changes can also be quite expensive. Hybrid cars are generally more expensive than equivalent petrol cars and things like solar panels for your home are still quite pricey. The cost of these things is slowly going down, but they are still not an option for many people.

Going green is on-trend this season...

So with more people wanting to help the environment, others not wanting to be inconvenienced and greener alternatives being expensive to set up, the energy resources we use are changing. Just not particularly quickly.

Q1   Give two reasons we currently do not use more renewable energy resources in the UK.   [2 marks]

Revision Questions for Section 1

Wow, that was a whole lot of Physics in one place — time to see how much of it you can remember.

- Try these questions and tick off each one when you get it right.
- When you've done all the questions under a heading and are completely happy, tick it off.

Motion (p.12-15) ☑

1) What is the difference between a scalar and a vector quantity? Give two examples of each.
2) Give the equation relating distance, speed and time.
3) Estimate typical speeds for a) walking, b) running, c) a car in a built-up area.
4) Define acceleration in terms of velocity and time.
5) What does the gradient represent for a) a distance/time graph? b) a velocity/time graph?
6) How would you find the distance travelled by an object from its velocity/time graph?

Newton's Laws, Forces and Momentum (p.16-21) ☑

7) State Newton's First and Second Laws of Motion.
8) Explain why cars have safety features to reduce the decelerations experienced by passengers.
9) What is the formula for calculating the weight of an object?
10) Explain why there must be a force acting to produce circular motion. What is the name of the force?
11) Describe an experiment to investigate Newton's Second Law of Motion.
12) What is inertia?
13) What is Newton's Third Law of Motion? Give an example of it in action.
14) State the formula used to calculate an object's momentum.
15) Explain the link between Newton's Third Law and conservation of momentum.

Car Safety (p.22-23) ☑

16) What is meant by a person's reaction time? Describe an experiment to measure reaction time.
17) State two factors that can affect the thinking distance for a stopping car.
18) State four things that can affect the braking distance of a vehicle.

Energy Stores, Transfers and Efficiency (p.24-27) ☑

19) What is the equation for calculating the energy in a moving object's kinetic energy store?
20) State the conservation of energy principle.
21) What is meant by the 'dissipation' of energy?
22) Describe the energy transfers when a ball is rolled up a slope.
23) Describe the energy transfers when a hair dryer is switched on.
24) Give the equation for the efficiency of a device.
25) How can you reduce unwanted energy transfers in a machine with moving, touching components?
26) How does the thermal conductivity of a wall affect its rate of energy transfer?

Energy Resources and Trends in their Use (p.28-30) ☐

27) What is the difference between renewable and non-renewable energy resources?
28) What are bio-fuels made from? Explain the benefits and drawbacks of using bio-fuels.
29) Give two benefits and two disadvantages of solar and wind power.
30) Explain why the UK plans to use more renewable energy resources in the future.

Wave Basics

Waves transfer <u>energy</u> from one place to another without transferring any <u>matter</u> (stuff). Clever so and so's.

Waves Transfer Energy and Information in the Direction they are Travelling

When waves travel through a medium, the <u>particles</u> of the medium <u>vibrate</u> and <u>transfer energy</u> and <u>information</u> between each other. BUT overall, the particles stay in the <u>same place</u>.

> For example, if you drop a twig into a calm pool of water, <u>ripples</u> form on, and <u>move</u> across, the water's surface. The ripples <u>don't</u> carry the <u>water</u> (or the twig) away with them though.
>
> Similarly, if you strum a <u>guitar string</u> and create a <u>sound wave</u>, the sound wave travels to your <u>ear</u> (so you can hear it) but it doesn't carry the <u>air</u> away from the guitar — if it did, it would create a <u>vacuum</u>.

1) The <u>amplitude</u> of a wave is the <u>displacement</u> from the <u>rest position</u> to a <u>crest</u> or <u>trough</u>.

2) The <u>wavelength</u> is the length of a <u>full cycle</u> of the wave (e.g. from <u>crest to crest</u>, or from <u>compression</u> to <u>compression</u> — see below).

3) <u>Frequency</u> is the <u>number of complete cycles</u> of the wave passing a certain point <u>per second</u>. Frequency is measured in <u>hertz</u> (<u>Hz</u>). 1 Hz is <u>1 wave per second</u>.

4) The <u>period</u> of a wave is the <u>number of seconds</u> it takes for <u>one full cycle</u>. <u>Period = 1 ÷ frequency</u>.

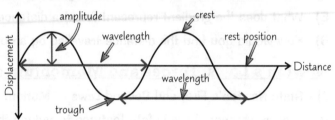

Transverse Waves Have Sideways Vibrations

In <u>transverse waves</u>, the vibrations are <u>perpendicular</u> (at **90°**) to the <u>direction</u> the wave travels. <u>Most waves</u> are transverse, including:
1) <u>All electromagnetic waves</u>, e.g. light (p.43).
2) <u>S-waves</u> (see p.37).
3) <u>Ripples</u> and waves in <u>water</u> (see p.33).

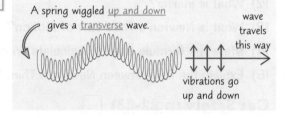

Longitudinal Waves Have Parallel Vibrations

1) In <u>longitudinal waves</u>, the vibrations are <u>parallel</u> to the <u>direction</u> the wave travels.

2) Examples are <u>sound waves</u> (p.35) and <u>P-waves</u> (p.37).

3) Longitudinal waves <u>squash up</u> and <u>stretch out</u> the arrangement of particles in the medium they pass through, making <u>compressions</u> (<u>high pressure</u>, lots of particles) and <u>rarefactions</u> (<u>low pressure</u>, fewer particles).

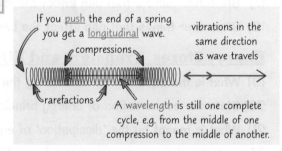

Wave Speed = Frequency × Wavelength

<u>Wave speed</u> is no different to any other speed — it tells you how <u>quickly</u> a <u>wave</u> moves through space. There are two ways to calculate wave speed:

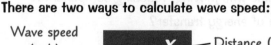
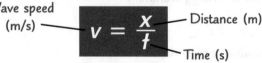
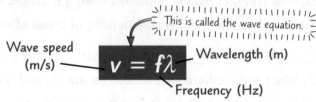

Wave speed (m/s) — $v = \dfrac{x}{t}$ — Distance (m), Time (s)

This is called the wave equation.

Wave speed (m/s) — $v = f\lambda$ — Wavelength (m), Frequency (Hz)

What about Mexican waves...

You won't get far unless you understand these wave basics. Try a question to test your knowledge.

Q1   A wave has a speed of 0.15 m/s and a wavelength of 7.5 cm. Calculate its frequency.   [3 marks]

Measuring Waves

The <u>speeds</u>, <u>frequencies</u> and <u>wavelengths</u> of waves can vary by huge amounts. So you have to use <u>suitable equipment</u> to measure waves in different materials, to make sure you get <u>accurate</u> and <u>precise</u> results.

Use an Oscilloscope to Measure the Speed of Sound

By attaching a <u>signal generator</u> to a speaker you can generate sounds with a specific <u>frequency</u>. You can use <u>two microphones</u> and an <u>oscilloscope</u> to find the <u>wavelength</u> of the sound waves generated.

1) Set up the oscilloscope so the <u>detected waves</u> at each microphone are shown as <u>separate waves</u>.

2) Start with <u>both microphones</u> next to the speaker, then slowly <u>move one away</u> until the two waves are <u>aligned</u> on the display, but have moved <u>exactly one wavelength apart</u>.

3) Measure the <u>distance between the microphones</u> to find one <u>wavelength</u> (λ).

4) You can then use the formula $v = f\lambda$ (p.32) to find the <u>speed</u> (v) of the <u>sound waves</u> passing through the <u>air</u> — the <u>frequency</u> (f) is whatever you set the <u>signal generator</u> to in the first place.

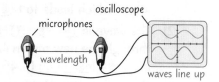

speaker attached to signal generator

microphones

oscilloscope

wavelength

waves line up

Measure the Speed of Water Ripples Using a Strobe Light

1) Using a <u>signal generator</u> attached to the <u>dipper</u> of a <u>ripple tank</u> you can create water waves at a <u>set frequency</u>.

2) Dim the lights and <u>turn on</u> the <u>strobe light</u> — you'll see a <u>wave pattern</u> made by the shadows of the <u>wave crests</u> on the screen below the tank.

3) Alter the <u>frequency</u> of the <u>strobe light</u> until the wave pattern on the screen appears to '<u>freeze</u>' and stop moving. This happens when the frequency of the waves and the strobe light are <u>equal</u> — the waves appear <u>not to move</u> because they are being lit at the <u>same point</u> in their cycle <u>each time</u>.

4) The distance between each shadow line is equal to one wavelength. Measure the <u>distance</u> between lines that are 10 wavelengths apart, then find the <u>average wavelength</u>.

5) Use $v = f\lambda$ to calculate the <u>speed</u> of the waves.

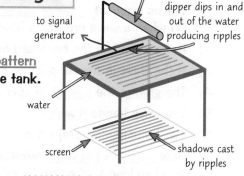

strobe light

dipper dips in and out of the water producing ripples

to signal generator

water

screen

shadows cast by ripples

You can find the frequency by using a regular light, so you can see the waves moving. Count how many waves pass a mark on the screen in a given time, then divide this by the time in seconds to find the frequency.

Use Peak Frequency to find the Speed of Waves in Solids

You can find the <u>speed of waves</u> in a <u>solid</u> by measuring the <u>frequency</u> of the <u>sound waves</u> produced when you hit the object, e.g. a rod, with a hammer. Hitting the rod causes <u>waves</u> to be produced <u>along</u> the rod. These waves make the rod <u>vibrate</u> and produce <u>sound waves</u> in the <u>air</u> around the rod (this is how a percussion triangle works). These <u>sound waves</u> have the <u>same frequencies</u> as the waves <u>in the rod</u>.

1) <u>Measure</u> and <u>record</u> the <u>length</u> of a <u>metal rod</u>, e.g. a brass rod.

2) Set up the apparatus shown in the diagram, making sure to secure the rod at its <u>centre</u>.

3) <u>Tap the rod</u> with the hammer. <u>Write down the peak frequency</u> displayed by the computer.

4) <u>Repeat</u> this three times to get an <u>average peak frequency</u>.

5) Calculate the <u>speed</u> of the wave using $v = f\lambda$, where λ is equal to <u>twice the length</u> of the rod.

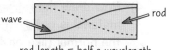

Lots of waves at lots of different frequencies are created in the rod when it is hit. The peak (loudest) frequency is created by this wave in the rod:

wave

rod

rod length = half a wavelength

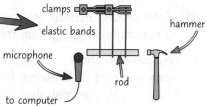

clamps

elastic bands

hammer

microphone

rod

to computer

My wave speed depends on how tired my arm is...

The sound and water waves experiments are really common, so make sure they're firmly stuck in your head.

Q1   Describe an experiment to measure the wavelength of a water wave.   [4 marks]

Wave Behaviour at Boundaries

When waves cross a boundary, they can be absorbed, transmitted, reflected, refracted... **Read on for more.**

Waves Are Absorbed, Transmitted and Reflected at Boundaries

When a wave meets a boundary between two materials (a material interface), three things can happen:

1) The wave is ABSORBED by the second material — the wave transfers energy to the material's energy stores. Often, the energy is transferred to a thermal energy store, which leads to heating (this is how a microwave works, see page 46).

2) The wave is TRANSMITTED through the second material — the wave carries on travelling through the new material. This often leads to refraction (see below). This can be used in communications (p.46) as well as in the lenses of glasses and cameras (p.41).

3) The wave is REFLECTED — this is where the incoming ray is neither absorbed or transmitted, but instead is 'sent back' away from the second material (see p.38). This is how echoes are created.

What actually happens depends on the wavelength of the wave and the properties of the materials involved.

Refraction — Waves Changing Direction at a Boundary

> You might see refraction of light talked about in terms of 'optical density'.

1) Waves travel at different speeds in materials with different densities. So when a wave crosses a boundary between materials it changes speed.

2) If the wave hits the boundary at an angle, this change of speed causes a change in direction — refraction.

3) If the wave is travelling along the normal it will change speed, but it's NOT refracted.

4) The greater the change in speed, the more a wave bends (changes direction).

5) The wave bends towards the normal if it slows down, and away from the normal if it speeds up.

6) Electromagnetic (EM) waves (see p.43) like light usually travel more slowly in denser materials.

7) How much an EM wave refracts can be affected by its wavelength — shorter wavelengths bend more. This can lead to the wavelengths spreading out (dispersion), e.g. white light becoming a spectrum.

8) The frequency of a wave stays the same when it crosses a boundary. As $v = f\lambda$, this means that the change in speed is caused by a change in wavelength — the wavelength decreases if the wave slows down, and increases if it speeds up.

A ray diagram shows the path that a wave travels. You can draw one for a refracted light ray:

1) First, start by drawing the boundary between your two materials and the normal (a line that is at 90° to the boundary).

2) Draw an incident ray that meets the normal at the boundary.

3) The angle between the ray and the normal is the angle of incidence. (If you're given this angle, make sure to draw it carefully using a protractor.)

4) Now draw the refracted ray on the other side of the boundary. If the second material is optically denser than the first, the refracted ray bends towards the normal (like on the right). The angle between the refracted ray and the normal (the angle of refraction) is smaller than the angle of incidence.

5) If the second material is less optically dense, the angle of refraction is larger than the angle of incidence.

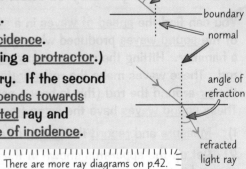

> There are more ray diagrams on p.42.

9) You can also show refraction using wave front diagrams. When one part of the wave front crosses a boundary into a denser material, that part travels slower than the rest of the wavefront, so the wave bends.

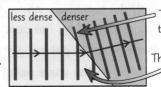

less dense \ denser

This part of the wave front travels slower than the rest.

The space between wave fronts shows the wavelength.

Red light bends the least — it should try yoga...

Refraction has loads of uses (e.g. in glasses, cameras and telescopes) so make sure you really understand it.

Q1   A light ray enters air from water at 50° to the normal. How does it bend relative to the normal?   [1 mark]

Sound

Time to learn all about the <u>properties</u> of <u>sound waves</u> and how they cause us to <u>hear</u> things. Don't panic though — you won't be quizzed on each individual part of the <u>ear</u>, just make sure you have a general idea.

Sound Travels as a Wave

1) <u>Sound waves</u> are caused by <u>vibrating objects</u>.

2) These vibrations are passed through the surrounding medium as a series of <u>compressions</u> and <u>rarefactions</u>. Sound waves are a type of <u>longitudinal wave</u> (see page 32).

3) When a sound wave travels <u>through a solid</u> it does so by causing <u>particles</u> in the solid to <u>vibrate</u>.

4) However, not all <u>frequencies</u> of sound can be transferred through an object. An object's <u>SIZE</u>, <u>SHAPE</u> and <u>STRUCTURE</u> determines which frequencies it can transmit.

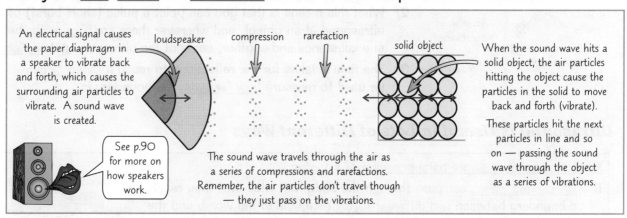

5) Sound travels at <u>different speeds</u> in <u>different media</u> — sound waves generally travel <u>faster</u> in <u>liquids</u> than they do in <u>gases</u>, and faster in <u>solids</u> than they do in <u>liquids</u>.

6) Like all waves, the <u>frequency</u> of sound <u>doesn't change</u> when it passes from one medium into another. But because $v = f\lambda$ the <u>wavelength</u> does — it gets <u>longer</u> when the wave <u>speeds up</u>, and <u>shorter</u> when it <u>slows down</u>.

7) So sound waves can <u>refract</u> as they enter <u>different media</u>. (However, since sound waves are always spreading out so much, the change in direction is <u>hard to spot</u> under normal circumstances.)

8) <u>Sound waves</u> will be <u>reflected</u> by <u>hard, flat surfaces</u>. Echoes are just reflected sound waves.

9) Sound can't travel in <u>space</u> because it's mostly a <u>vacuum</u> (there are no particles to move or vibrate).

You Hear Sound When Your Eardrum Vibrates

1) Sound waves that reach your <u>eardrum</u> cause it to <u>vibrate</u>.

2) These <u>vibrations</u> are passed on to <u>tiny bones</u> in your ear called <u>ossicles</u>, through the <u>semicircular canals</u> and to the <u>cochlea</u>.

3) The <u>cochlea</u> turns these vibrations into <u>electrical signals</u> which get sent to your <u>brain</u>.

4) The brain <u>interprets</u> the signals as sounds of different <u>pitches</u> and <u>volumes</u>, depending on their <u>frequency</u> and <u>intensity</u>. A <u>higher frequency</u> sound wave has a <u>higher pitch</u>.

5) <u>Human hearing</u> is limited by the <u>size</u> and <u>shape</u> of our <u>eardrum</u>, and the <u>structure</u> of all the parts within the ear that <u>vibrate</u> to transmit the sound wave.

Sorry, listening to music doesn't count as revision...

Make sure you know that sound waves make solids vibrate and that your vibrating eardrum lets you hear them.

Q1   Briefly describe how you hear a sound wave.   [3 marks]

Ultrasound

Can you hear <u>that</u>? If not, '<u>that</u>' could be <u>ultrasound</u> — a handy wave used for <u>seeing hidden objects</u>.

Ultrasound *is Sound with Frequencies Higher Than 20 000 Hz*

Electrical devices can be made that produce <u>electrical oscillations</u> of <u>any frequency</u>.
These can easily be converted into <u>mechanical vibrations</u> to produce <u>sound</u> waves <u>above 20 000 Hz</u>
(i.e. above the range of human hearing). This is called <u>ultrasound</u> and it pops up all over the place.

Ultrasound *Waves Get Partially Reflected at Boundaries*

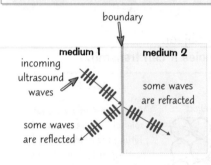

boundary
medium 1   medium 2
incoming
ultrasound
waves
some waves
are refracted
some waves
are reflected

1) When a wave passes from one medium into another, <u>some</u> of the wave is <u>reflected</u> off the boundary between the two media, and some is transmitted (and refracted). This is <u>partial reflection</u>.

2) What this means is that you can point a pulse (short burst) of ultrasound at an object, and wherever there are <u>boundaries</u> between one substance and another, some of the ultrasound gets <u>reflected back</u>.

3) The time it takes for the reflections to reach a <u>detector</u> can be used to measure <u>how far away</u> the boundary is.

Ultrasound *is Useful in Lots of Different Ways*

<u>Medical imaging, e.g. pre-natal scanning of a foetus</u>

1) <u>Ultrasound waves</u> can pass through the body, but whenever they reach a boundary between <u>two different media</u> (like fluid in the womb and the skin of the foetus) some of the wave is <u>reflected back</u> and <u>detected</u>.

2) The exact <u>timing and distribution</u> of these <u>echoes</u> are processed by a computer to produce a <u>video image</u> of the foetus.

3) So far as we know, ultrasound imaging like this is <u>completely safe</u>.

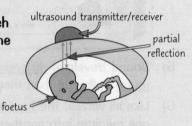

ultrasound transmitter/receiver
partial
reflection
foetus

<u>Industrial imaging, e.g. finding flaws in materials</u>

1) Ultrasound can also be used to find <u>flaws</u> in objects such as <u>pipes</u>, or <u>materials</u> such as wood or metal.

2) Ultrasound waves entering a material will usually be <u>reflected</u> by the <u>far side</u> of the material.

3) If there is a flaw such as a <u>crack</u> inside the object, the waves will be <u>reflected sooner</u>.

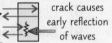

ultrasound waves reflected
by far side of material
crack causes
early reflection
of waves

Ultrasound is also used in <u>echo sounding</u>, which is a type of <u>sonar</u> used by boats and submarines to find out the <u>distance to the seabed</u> or to <u>locate</u> objects in <u>deep water</u>.

EXAMPLE:

A pulse of ultrasound takes 4.5 seconds to travel from a submarine to the sea bed and back again. If the speed of sound in seawater is 1520 m/s, how far away is the submarine from the seabed?

1) The 4.5 s is for there <u>and</u> back, so <u>halve</u> the time. $4.5 \div 2 = 2.25$ s
2) Use the <u>wave speed formula</u> from p.32. $x = vt = 1520 \times 2.25$
$= 3420$ m

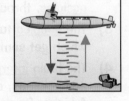

Partially reflected — completely revised...

Ultrasound waves are really useful, so make sure you can describe how looking at the time taken for them to be reflected can let you see the structure of things you would otherwise be unable to — like the inside of a metal.

Q1   Calculate how long it takes for an ultrasound pulse to return to a submarine from the seabed, if the speed of sound in seawater is 1520 m/s and the submarine is 2500 m above the seabed.   [3 marks]

Infrasound and Seismic Waves

Studying the paths of certain types of <u>wave</u> through structures can give you clues to some of the properties of the structure that you can't <u>see</u> by eye. You've already seen this with <u>ultrasound</u>, time for some more.

Infrasound is Sound with Frequencies Lower Than 20 Hz

1) <u>Infrasound</u> waves are sound waves <u>so low</u> in <u>frequency</u> that we can't hear them — they're <u>under 20 Hz</u>.

2) Some <u>animals</u> communicate using infrasound — for example <u>elephants</u> and <u>whales</u>. By detecting infrasound, scientists are able to <u>track</u> these animals for conservation purposes.

3) Natural events like erupting <u>volcanoes</u>, <u>avalanches</u> and <u>earthquakes</u> also produce infrasound in the local area. Scientists can <u>monitor infrasound</u> to try to <u>predict</u> events, e.g. if a volcano will shortly erupt.

4) <u>Earthquakes</u> also produce waves that travel through the <u>different layers</u> of the Earth. Some of these waves have frequencies less than 20 Hz — i.e. they're <u>infrasound waves</u>. We can use these waves to explore the <u>structure</u> of the <u>Earth</u> (see below).

Earthquakes and Explosions Cause Seismic Waves

1) When there's an <u>earthquake</u> somewhere, it produces <u>seismic waves</u> at a <u>range of frequencies</u> which travel out through the Earth. We <u>detect</u> these waves all over the surface of the planet using <u>seismometers</u>.

2) <u>Seismologists</u> work out the <u>time</u> it takes for the waves to reach each seismometer. They also note which parts of the Earth <u>don't receive the waves</u> at all.

3) When <u>seismic waves</u> reach a <u>boundary</u> between different layers of <u>material</u> (which all have different <u>properties</u>, like density) inside the Earth, some waves will be <u>absorbed</u> and some will be <u>refracted</u>.

4) Most of the time, if the waves are <u>refracted</u>, they change speed <u>gradually</u>, resulting in a <u>curved path</u>. But when the properties change <u>suddenly</u>, the wave speed changes abruptly, and the path has a <u>kink</u>.

P-waves Can Travel Through the Earth's Core, S-waves Can't

1) The main <u>two</u> seismic waves you need to know about are <u>P-waves</u> and <u>S-waves</u>.

2) By observing how seismic waves are <u>absorbed</u> and <u>refracted</u>, scientists have been able to work out <u>where</u> the properties of the Earth change <u>dramatically</u>. Our current understanding of the <u>internal structure</u> of the Earth and the <u>size</u> of the <u>Earth's core</u> is based on these <u>observations</u>.

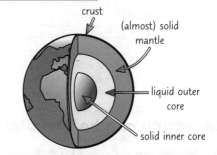

crust
(almost) solid mantle
liquid outer core
solid inner core

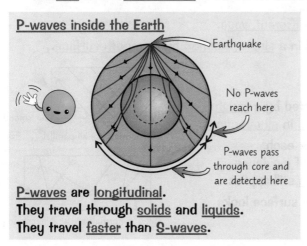

P-waves inside the Earth

Earthquake

No P-waves reach here

P-waves pass through core and are detected here

<u>P-waves</u> are <u>longitudinal</u>.
They travel through <u>solids</u> and <u>liquids</u>.
They travel <u>faster</u> than <u>S-waves</u>.

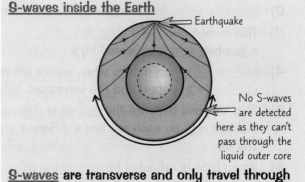

<u>S-waves inside the Earth</u>

Earthquake

No S-waves are detected here as they can't pass through the liquid outer core

<u>S-waves</u> are transverse and only travel through <u>solids</u>. They're <u>slower</u> than <u>P-waves</u>.

I'll take an Earth with a gooey filling and a crispy crust to go...

Wow, who knew earthquakes could be so educational as well as destructive...

Q1 S-waves produced at the Earth's North Pole would not be detected at the South Pole. Suggest one conclusion you can make about the Earth's core from the observation. Explain your answer. [2 marks]

Reflection

If you're anything like me, you'll have spent hours gazing into a <u>mirror</u> in wonder. Here's why...

You Can Draw a Simple Ray Diagram for Reflection

1) The <u>law of reflection</u> is true for <u>all</u> reflected waves:

> **Angle of incidence = Angle of reflection**

2) <u>The angle of incidence</u> is the angle between the <u>incoming wave</u> and the <u>normal</u>.

3) <u>The angle of reflection</u> is the angle between the <u>reflected wave</u> and the normal.

4) The <u>normal</u> is an <u>imaginary line</u> that's <u>perpendicular</u> (at right angles) to the <u>surface</u> at the <u>point of incidence</u> (the point where the wave <u>hits</u> the boundary).

5) The normal is usually shown as a <u>dotted line</u>.

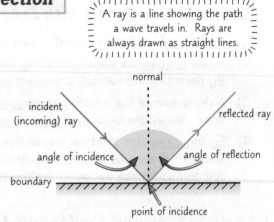

A ray is a line showing the path a wave travels in. Rays are always drawn as straight lines.

Total Internal Reflection Depends on the Critical Angle

1) A wave hitting a surface can experience <u>total internal reflection</u> (it is reflected back into the material).

2) This can only happen when the wave travels <u>through a dense material</u> like glass or water towards a <u>less dense</u> substance like air, and the <u>angle of incidence</u>, *i*, is <u>larger</u> than a certain angle, called the <u>critical angle</u>. Every boundary has its <u>own</u>, <u>different</u> critical angle.

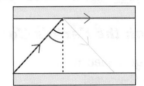

If *i* is <u>less</u> than the critical angle

Most of the light is <u>refracted</u> into the outer layer, but some of it is <u>internally reflected</u>.

If *i* is <u>equal to</u> the critical angle

The ray would go <u>along the surface</u> (with quite a bit of <u>internal reflection</u> as well).

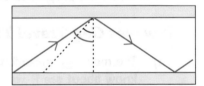

If *i* is <u>larger</u> than the critical angle

<u>No light comes out</u>. It's <u>all</u> internally reflected, i.e. <u>total internal reflection</u>.

Reflection can be Specular or Diffuse

1) Waves are <u>reflected</u> by <u>different boundaries</u> in <u>different ways</u>.

2) <u>Specular reflection</u> is when waves are reflected in a <u>single direction</u> by a <u>smooth surface</u>.

3) This means you get a <u>clear reflection</u>, e.g. when <u>light</u> is reflected by a <u>mirror</u>.

4) <u>Diffuse reflection</u> occurs when waves are reflected by a <u>rough surface</u> (e.g. paper) and the waves are <u>reflected</u> in <u>all directions</u>.

5) This happens because the <u>normal</u> is <u>different</u> for each incident ray, so each ray has a different <u>angle of incidence</u>. The rule <u>angle of incidence = angle of reflection</u> still applies.

6) When light is reflected by <u>something rough</u>, the surface looks <u>matt</u>, and you <u>don't</u> get a clear reflection.

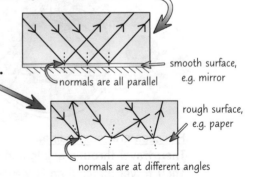

smooth surface, e.g. mirror

normals are all parallel

rough surface, e.g. paper

normals are at different angles

My reflection is absolutely spec<small>t</small>acular...

Remember, the angle of incidence is always equal to the angle of reflection of a wave.

Q1   Name the type of reflection that occurs when waves are reflected by a smooth mirror.   [1 mark]

Q2   A light ray is incident on a mirror at an angle of 30°. Draw a ray diagram to show its reflection.   [3 marks]

Investigating Refraction

Hurrah — it's time to whip out your ray box and get some refraction going on. This is just one practical that covers how electromagnetic waves behave — there's another one over on page 44.

You Need to Do This Experiment in a Dim Room

1) This experiment uses a ray of light, so it's best to do it in a dim room so you can clearly see the ray.

2) The ray of light must be thin, so you can easily see the middle of the ray when tracing it and measuring angles from it.

3) To do this, you can use a ray box — an enclosed box that contains a light bulb. A thin slit is cut into one of the sides — allowing a thin ray of light out of the box that you can use for your experiment.

You Can Use a Glass Block to Investigate Refraction

Light is refracted at the boundary between air and glass. You can investigate this by looking at how much light is refracted when it passes through a glass block.

1) Place a rectangular glass block on a piece of paper and trace around it. Use a ray box to shine a ray of light at the middle of one side of the block.

2) Trace the incident ray and the emergent ray on the other side of the block. Remove the block and, with a straight line, join up the incident ray and the emergent ray to show the path of the refracted ray through the block.

3) Draw the normal at the point where the light ray entered the block. Use a protractor to measure the angle between the incident ray and the normal (the angle of incidence, *I*) and the angle between the refracted ray and the normal (the angle of refraction, *R*).

4) Do the same for the point where the ray emerges from the block.

5) Repeat this three times, keeping the angle of incidence as the ray enters the block the same.

6) Calculate an average for each of the angles.

You should draw...

incident ray

normal ......

I

R) refracted ray

I

.... normal

R

emergent ray

‖‖‖‖‖‖‖‖‖‖‖‖‖‖‖
Head over to page 34 for a reminder about refraction.
‖‖‖‖‖‖‖‖‖‖‖‖‖‖

- You should see that the ray of light bends towards the normal as it enters the block (so the angle of refraction is less than the angle of incidence). This is because air has one of the lowest optical densities that there is (p.34) so the light ray will almost always slow down when it enters the block.

- You should then see the ray of light bends away from the normal as it leaves the block. This is because the light ray speeds up as it leaves the block and travels through the air.

- It's important to remember that all electromagnetic waves can be refracted — this experiment uses visible light so that you can actually see the ray being refracted as it travels through the block.

Bonus tip: glass also slows down pesky bugs.

Lights, camera, refraction...

This experiment isn't the trickiest, but you still have to be able to describe how to do it and what it shows.

Q1   a) Describe an experiment you could do to measure how much light is refracted when it enters a glass block. [3 marks]

b) Explain why a thin beam of light should be used. [1 mark]

Visible Light and Colour

The <u>colour</u> something appears to be is all about what <u>wavelengths</u> of light we're <u>seeing</u> when we look at it.

Colour and Transparency Depend on Absorbed Wavelengths

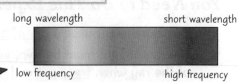

long wavelength   short wavelength

low frequency   high frequency

1) <u>Colour</u> is about differences in <u>absorption</u>, <u>transmission</u> and <u>reflection</u> of <u>different wavelengths</u> by <u>different materials</u>.

2) <u>White light</u> is a mixture of <u>all</u> the different <u>colours</u> of light, which all have <u>different wavelengths</u>.

3) Different objects <u>absorb</u>, <u>transmit</u> and <u>reflect</u> different <u>wavelengths</u> of light in different ways.

4) <u>Opaque</u> objects are objects that <u>do not transmit light</u>. When visible light waves hit them, they <u>absorb</u> some wavelengths of light and <u>reflect</u> others.

5) The <u>colour</u> of an opaque object depends on <u>which wavelengths</u> of light are <u>reflected</u>. E.g. a red apple appears to be red because the wavelengths corresponding to the <u>red part</u> of the <u>visible spectrum</u> are reflected.

6) Colours can also <u>mix together</u> to make other colours. The only colours you <u>can't</u> make by mixing are the <u>primary</u> colours: pure <u>red</u>, <u>green</u> and <u>blue</u>. So a banana may look <u>yellow</u> because it's <u>reflecting yellow light</u> OR because it's reflecting <u>both red and green light</u>.

7) <u>White</u> objects <u>reflect all</u> of the wavelengths of visible light <u>equally</u>.

8) <u>Black</u> objects <u>absorb all</u> wavelengths of visible light. Your eyes see black as the <u>lack of</u> any visible light (i.e. the lack of any <u>colour</u>).

How I love my coat that reflects different wavelengths of li-ight!!!

9) <u>Transparent</u> (see-through) and <u>translucent</u> (partially see-through) objects <u>transmit light</u>, i.e. not all light that hits the surface of the object is absorbed or reflected — some (or most for transparent objects) can <u>pass through</u>.

10) Some wavelengths of light may be <u>absorbed</u> or <u>reflected</u> by translucent and (to a lesser extent) transparent objects. These objects will appear to be the colour of light that corresponds to the wavelengths most <u>strongly transmitted</u> by the object.

Colour Filters Only Let Through Particular Wavelengths

white light

BLUE FILTER

All other colours are absorbed by the filter.

Blue light is transmitted.

1) Colour filters are used to <u>filter out</u> different <u>wavelengths</u> of light, so that only certain colours (wavelengths) are <u>transmitted</u> — the rest are <u>absorbed</u>.

2) A <u>primary colour filter</u> only <u>transmits</u> that <u>colour</u>, e.g. if <u>white light</u> is shone at a <u>blue</u> colour filter, <u>only</u> blue light will be let through. The rest of the light will be <u>absorbed</u>.

3) If you look at a <u>blue object</u> through a blue <u>colour filter</u>, it would still look <u>blue</u>. Blue light is <u>reflected</u> from the object's surface and is <u>transmitted</u> by the filter.

4) However, if the object was e.g. <u>red</u> (or any colour <u>not made from blue light</u>), the object would appear <u>black</u> when viewed through a blue filter. <u>All</u> of the light <u>reflected</u> by the object will be <u>absorbed</u> by the filter.

5) <u>Filters</u> that <u>aren't</u> for <u>primary</u> colours let through <u>both</u> the <u>wavelengths</u> of light corresponding to that <u>colour</u> and the wavelengths of the <u>primary</u> colours that can be added together to make that colour. E.g. <u>cyan</u> can be made from <u>blue</u> and <u>green</u> light mixed together. So a <u>cyan</u> colour filter will let through the <u>wavelengths</u> of light that correspond to <u>cyan</u>, <u>blue</u> and <u>green</u>.

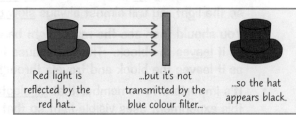

Red light is reflected by the red hat...   ...but it's not transmitted by the blue colour filter...   ...so the hat appears black.

Have you seen my white shirt? It's red and yellow and green and...

Hopefully you now know enough about absorption and reflection that you're feeling pretty confident. Once you've got them down, this page is pretty easy — red objects reflect red light and red filters let red light through. Simple.

Q1 a) Explain why a cucumber looks green.   [2 marks]

b) State the colour a cucumber would look if you looked at it through a red filter.   [1 mark]

Lenses

Lenses bring light rays to a <u>focus</u> or <u>spread them out</u>. Which is <u>pretty darn useful</u>, I can tell you.

Different Lenses Produce Different Kinds of Image

Lenses form images by <u>refracting</u> light (p.34) and changing its direction. There are <u>two main types</u> of lens — <u>converging</u> and <u>diverging</u>. They have different shapes and have <u>opposite effects</u> on light rays.

1) A <u>converging</u> lens <u>bulges outwards</u> in the middle. It causes parallel rays of <u>light</u> to be <u>brought together</u> (<u>converge</u>) at the <u>principal focus</u>. They're sometimes called <u>convex</u> lenses.

2) A <u>diverging</u> (or concave) lens <u>caves inwards</u>. It causes parallel rays of <u>light</u> to <u>spread out</u> (<u>diverge</u>).

3) The <u>axis</u> of a lens is a line passing through the <u>middle</u> of the lens.

4) The <u>principal focus</u> of a <u>converging lens</u> is where rays hitting the lens parallel to the axis all <u>meet</u>.

5) The <u>principal focus</u> of a <u>diverging lens</u> is the point where rays hitting the lens parallel to the axis <u>appear</u> to all <u>come from</u> — you can trace them back until they all appear to <u>meet up</u> at a point behind the lens.

6) There is a principal focus on <u>each side</u> of the lens. The <u>distance</u> from the <u>centre of the lens</u> to the <u>principal focus</u> (F) is called the <u>focal length</u>.

<u>Converging Lens</u>

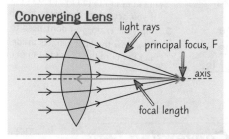

light rays

principal focus, F

axis

focal length

<u>Diverging Lens</u>

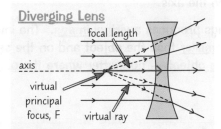

focal length

axis

virtual principal focus, F

virtual ray

When a ray enters any lens, it bends towards the normal. When it leaves, it bends away from the normal (p.34).

To describe an image, say if it's bigger or smaller than the object, if it's upright or inverted and if it's real or virtual.

<u>Images</u> are formed at points where <u>all</u> the light rays from a <u>certain point</u> on an object appear to come together.

There are <u>two types</u> of images that can be formed by lenses:

1) A <u>REAL</u> image is formed when the light rays <u>actually come together</u> to form the image. The image can be <u>captured on a screen</u>, because the <u>light rays actually meet</u> at the place where the image seems to be. E.g. the image formed on the eye's retina.

object

real image on screen

2) A <u>VIRTUAL</u> image is when the light rays from the object <u>appear</u> to be coming from a completely <u>different place</u> to where they're <u>actually</u> coming from. The light rays <u>don't actually come together</u> at the point where the image seems to be, so it <u>cannot be captured</u> on a screen. E.g. <u>magnifying glasses</u> create <u>virtual images</u>.

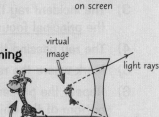

virtual image

light rays

object

The Power of a Lens Increases with its Curvature

1) Focal length is related to the <u>power</u> of the lens. The more <u>powerful</u> the lens, the more <u>strongly</u> it converges rays of light, so the <u>shorter the focal length</u>.

2) For a <u>converging lens</u>, the power is <u>positive</u>. For a <u>diverging lens</u>, the power is <u>negative</u>.

3) The curvature of a lens affects its power. To make a <u>more powerful</u> lens from a <u>certain material</u> like glass, you just have to make it with more <u>strongly curved surfaces</u>.

4) Some <u>materials</u> are <u>better</u> at focusing light than others. This means <u>powerful lenses</u> can be made <u>thinner</u> by <u>changing the material</u> they're made from (using a material that's better at focusing light means you don't need to make the lens as <u>curved</u> to get the <u>same focal length</u>).

He's magnificent, that pug...

Make sure you know the differences between real and virtual images — they can be pretty tough.

Q1   What is the principal focus of: a) a converging lens   b) a diverging lens?   [2 marks]

Q2   Sketch parallel rays of light being focused by a converging lens.   [2 marks]

Lenses and Ray Diagrams

You need to be able to draw <u>ray diagrams</u> for <u>converging</u> and <u>diverging lenses</u> too.

Draw a Ray Diagram for an Image Through a Diverging Lens

1) Pick a point on the <u>top</u> of the object. Draw a ray going from the object to the lens <u>parallel</u> to the axis of the lens.

2) Draw another ray from the <u>top</u> of the object going right through the <u>middle</u> of the lens.

3) The incident ray that's <u>parallel</u> to the axis is <u>refracted</u> so it appears to have come from the <u>principal focus</u> (F). Draw a <u>ray</u> from the principal focus. Make it <u>dotted</u> before it reaches the lens (as it's virtual here).

4) The ray passing through the <u>middle</u> of the lens <u>doesn't bend</u>.

5) Mark where this ray meets the <u>virtual ray</u>. That's the <u>top</u> of the image.

6) <u>Repeat</u> the process for a point on the <u>bottom</u> of the object. When the bottom of the object is on the <u>axis</u>, the bottom of the image is <u>also</u> on the axis.

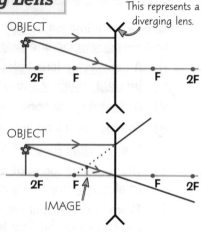

This represents a diverging lens.

If you get a lens that looks like this in your exam, you don't need to show how the light refracts inside it.

A <u>diverging</u> lens always produces a <u>virtual image</u>. The image is <u>the right way up</u>, <u>smaller</u> than the object and on the <u>same side of the lens as the object</u> — <u>no matter where the object is</u>.

Draw a Ray Diagram for an Image Through a Converging Lens

1) Pick a point on the <u>top</u> of the object. Draw a ray going from the object to the lens <u>parallel</u> to the axis of the lens.

2) Draw another ray from the <u>top</u> of the object going right through the <u>middle</u> of the lens.

3) The incident ray that's <u>parallel</u> to the axis is <u>refracted</u> through the <u>principal focus</u> (F). Draw a <u>refracted ray</u> passing through F.

4) The ray passing through the <u>middle</u> of the lens doesn't bend.

5) Mark where the rays <u>meet</u>. That's the <u>top of the image</u>.

6) Repeat the process for a point on the bottom of the object. When the bottom of the object is on the <u>axis</u>, the bottom of the image is <u>also</u> on the axis.

This is another way of drawing a converging lens.

The <u>distance</u> from the lens to the <u>object</u> affects the <u>size</u> and <u>position</u> of the <u>image</u>:

1) An object <u>2F</u> (two focal lengths) from the lens produces a <u>real</u>, <u>inverted</u> (upside down) image the <u>same size</u> as the object and <u>at 2F</u> on the other side of the lens.

2) An object <u>between F and 2F</u> will make a <u>real</u>, <u>inverted</u> image <u>bigger</u> than the object and <u>beyond 2F</u>.

3) An object <u>nearer than F</u> will make a <u>virtual</u> image the <u>right way up</u>, <u>bigger</u> than the object and on the <u>same side</u> of the lens.

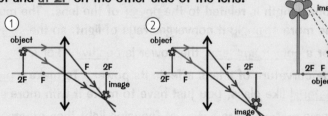

Warning — too much revision can cause a loss of focus...

Congratulations, you've reached the end of lenses. Why not celebrate with some practice questions?

Q1   What kind of image does a diverging lens produce?   [1 mark]

Q2   Draw a ray diagram for an object at a distance of 0.5F in front of a converging lens.   [3 marks]

Electromagnetic Waves

You've learned a lot about light so far, but light's just one small part of the EM spectrum...

There's a Continuous Spectrum of EM Waves

1) Electromagnetic (EM) waves are transverse waves (p.32).

2) They all travel at the same speed through a vacuum (space). But they travel at different speeds in different materials (which can lead to refraction and dispersion, p.34).

Electromagnetic waves aren't vibrations of particles, they're vibrations of electric (p.84) and magnetic (p.85) fields. This means they can travel through a vacuum.

3) EM waves vary in wavelength from around 10^{-15} m to more than 10^4 m.

4) We group them based on their wavelength and frequency — there are seven basic types, but the different groups merge to form a continuous spectrum.

5) EM waves are generated by a variety of changes in atoms and their nuclei, giving a large range of frequencies. E.g. changes in the nucleus of an atom create gamma rays (p.51) and visible light is often produced by changes in an electron's energy level (p.50). This also explains why atoms can absorb a range of frequencies — each one causes a different change.

6) Our eyes can only detect a small part of this spectrum — visible light. Different colours of light have different wavelengths — from longest to shortest: red, orange, yellow, green, blue, indigo, violet.

RADIO WAVES	MICRO WAVES	INFRA RED	VISIBLE LIGHT	ULTRA VIOLET	X-RAYS	GAMMA RAYS
1 m – 10^4 m	10^{-2} m	10^{-5} m	10^{-7} m	10^{-8} m	10^{-10} m	10^{-15} m

wavelength

long wavelength, low frequency → short wavelength, high frequency

7) All EM waves transfer energy from a source to an absorber. For example, when you warm yourself by an electric heater, infrared waves transfer energy from the thermal energy store of the heater (the source) to your thermal energy store (the absorber).

8) The higher the frequency of the EM wave, the more energy it transfers (and so the more dangerous it is for humans — see below).

Different EM Waves Have Different Properties

EM waves are sometimes called EM radiation.

As you saw on p.34, when EM waves meet a boundary they can be absorbed, transmitted, refracted or reflected. What happens depends on the materials at the boundary and the wavelength of the EM wave — e.g. some materials absorb some wavelengths of light but reflect others. This is what causes things to be a certain colour (p.40).

Differences in how EM waves are transmitted, reflected and absorbed have implications for human health:

1) Radio waves are transmitted through the body without being absorbed.

2) Some wavelengths of microwaves can be absorbed, causing heating of cells, which may be dangerous.

3) Infrared (IR) and visible light are mostly reflected or absorbed by the skin, causing some heating too. IR can cause burns if the skin gets too hot.

Most of the UV radiation produced by the Sun that hits the Earth's atmosphere gets absorbed.

4) Ultraviolet (UV) is also absorbed by the skin. But it has a higher frequency, so it is potentially more dangerous. It's a type of ionising radiation (p.50) and when absorbed it can cause damage to cells on the surface of your skin, which could lead to skin cancer. It can also damage your eyes and cause a variety of eye conditions or even blindness.

5) X-rays and gamma rays are also ionising, so they can cause mutations and damage cells too (which can lead to cancer). But they have even higher frequencies, so transfer even more energy, causing even more damage. They can also pass through the skin and be absorbed by deeper tissues.

Learn about the EM spectrum and wave goodbye to exam woe...

Here's a handy mnemonic for the order of EM waves: 'Rock Music Is Very Useful for eXperiments with Goats'.

Q1   Explain why gamma rays are more dangerous to humans than visible light.   [2 marks]

Emitting and Absorbing EM Radiation

You, me, the cat, we all emit radiation. And it's vital to keeping us at a fairly constant temperature.

Every Object Absorbs and Emits EM Radiation

1) ALL objects are continually emitting (radiating) and absorbing EM radiation over a range of wavelengths.

2) The distribution and intensity of these wavelengths ONLY depends on the object's temperature. Intensity is the power per unit area (power is energy transferred per second, p.66).

3) As the temperature of an object increases, the intensity of every emitted wavelength increases.

4) However, the intensity increases more rapidly for shorter wavelengths than longer wavelengths. This causes the peak wavelength (the wavelength with the highest intensity) to decrease.

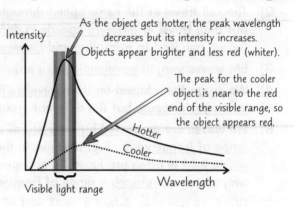

As the object gets hotter, the peak wavelength decreases but its intensity increases. Objects appear brighter and less red (whiter).

The peak for the cooler object is near to the red end of the visible range, so the object appears red.

5) The rate at which an object absorbs and radiates EM radiation also affects its temperature:

• If the average power that the object absorbs is more than the average power that it radiates, the object heats up. If the average power radiated is larger than the average power absorbed, the object cools down.

• An object at a constant temperature radiates and absorbs the same average power.

Radiation Affects the Earth's Temperature

1) The overall temperature of the Earth depends on the amount of radiation it reflects, absorbs and emits.

2) During the day, lots of radiation (including light) is transferred to the Earth from the Sun.

3) Some of this is reflected, but most of it is absorbed. The radiation is reflected and absorbed by the Earth's ATMOSPHERE, CLOUDS and SURFACE. This causes an increase in local temperature.

4) At night, radiation is emitted by the atmosphere, clouds and the Earth's surface. This causes a decrease in the local temperature.

5) Overall, the temperature of the Earth stays fairly constant.

6) Changes to the atmosphere can cause a change to the Earth's overall temperature. If the atmosphere starts to absorb more radiation without emitting the same amount, the overall temperature will rise until absorption and emission are equal again.

Black Surfaces are Better Emitters than White Ones

PRACTICAL

You can investigate how well different surfaces emit radiation with this simple experiment:

1) Wrap four identical test tubes with material, e.g. paper. The material covering each test tube should be the same, but each one should have a different surface or be a different colour, e.g. black and white paper, glossy and matte paper.

2) Boil water in a kettle and fill each test tube with the same volume of water.

3) Use a thermometer to measure the temperature of the water in the test tubes every minute. Seal the test tubes with bungs between measurements.

The temperature of the water will decrease quicker for the test tubes surrounded by surfaces that are good emitters of radiation. You should find that matte (or dull) surfaces are better emitters than shiny ones and that black surfaces emit radiation better than white ones.

Feelin' hot hot hot...

Get that link between radiation and temperature firmly stuck in your head. Then have a go at this question:

Q1 Explain what is happening in terms of radiation and temperature when a bowl of ice cream is left on a counter in a warm room.

[2 marks]

EM Waves for Communication

Different EM waves have different properties, which make them useful to us in different ways.

Radio Waves are Made by Oscillating Charges

1) EM waves are made up of oscillating electric and magnetic fields.

2) Alternating currents (a.c.) (p.79) are made up of oscillating charges. As the charges oscillate, they produce oscillating electric and magnetic fields, i.e. electromagnetic waves.

3) The frequency of the waves produced will be equal to the frequency of the alternating current.

4) You can produce radio waves using an alternating current in an electrical circuit. The object in which charges (electrons) oscillate to create the radio waves is called a transmitter.

5) When transmitted radio waves reach a receiver, the radio waves are absorbed.

6) The energy carried by the waves is transferred to the electrons in the material of the receiver.

7) This energy causes the electrons to oscillate and, if the receiver is part of a complete electrical circuit, it generates an alternating current.

8) This current has the same frequency as the radio wave that generated it.

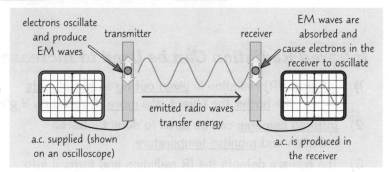

Radio Waves are Used Mainly for Communication and Broadcasting

1) Long-wave radio (wavelengths of 1 – 10 km) can be received halfway round the world from where they started, because long wavelengths bend around the curved surface of the Earth. This makes it possible for radio signals to be received even if the receiver isn't in the line of sight of the transmitter.

2) Short-wave radio signals (wavelengths of about 10 m – 100 m) can, like long-wave, be received at long distances from the transmitter. That's because they are reflected by the Earth's atmosphere.

3) Bluetooth® uses short-wave radio waves to send data over short distances between devices without wires (e.g. wireless headsets so you can use your phone while driving a car).

4) The radio waves used for TV and FM radio transmissions have very short wavelengths. To get reception, you must be in direct sight of the transmitter — the signal doesn't bend or travel far through buildings.

Microwaves and Radio Waves are Used by Satellites

1) Communication to and from satellites (including satellite TV signals and satellite phones) uses EM waves which can pass easily through the Earth's watery atmosphere.

2) These waves are usually microwaves, but can sometimes be relatively high frequency radio waves.

3) For satellite TV, the signal from a transmitter is transmitted into space and picked up by the satellite receiver dish orbiting thousands of kilometres above the Earth.

4) The satellite transmits the signal back to Earth in a different direction, where it's received by a satellite dish on the ground.

Size matters — and my wave's longer than yours...

Producing radio waves — who knew it was so tricky? It's worth it though — they're just so darn useful.

Q1   Explain why signals between satellites are usually transmitted as microwaves.   [1 mark]

Microwaves and Infrared

Haven't had enough <u>uses of EM waves</u>? Good, because here are just a few more uses of those incredibly handy waves — complete with the all-important <u>reasons</u> for why they have been used. Get learning.

Microwave Ovens Also Use Microwaves

1) In <u>microwave ovens</u>, the microwaves are <u>absorbed</u> by <u>water molecules</u> in food.

2) The microwaves penetrate up to a few centimetres into the food before being <u>absorbed</u> and <u>transferring</u> the energy they are carrying to the <u>water molecules</u> in the food, causing the water to <u>heat up</u>.

3) The water molecules then <u>transfer</u> this energy to the rest of the molecules in the food <u>by heating</u> — which <u>quickly cooks</u> the food.

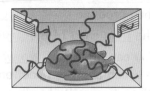

Infrared Radiation Can be Used to Increase or Monitor Temperature

1) <u>Infrared</u> (IR) radiation is <u>given out</u> by all <u>hot objects</u> — and the <u>hotter</u> the object, the <u>more</u> IR radiation it gives out.

2) <u>Infrared cameras</u> can be used to detect infrared radiation and <u>monitor temperature</u>.

3) The camera detects the IR radiation and turns it into an <u>electrical signal</u>, which is <u>displayed on a screen</u> as a picture. This is called <u>thermal imaging</u>.

4) <u>Thermal imaging</u> is used by police to see suspects that are trying to <u>escape or hide in the dark</u>.

5) <u>Infrared sensors</u> can be used in <u>security systems</u>. If a change in infrared radiation is detected, an <u>alarm</u> sounds or a <u>security light</u> turns on.

Different colours represent different amounts of IR radiation being detected. Here, the redder the colour, the more infrared radiation is being detected.

6) <u>Absorbing</u> IR radiation causes objects to get <u>hotter</u>. <u>Food</u> can be <u>cooked</u> using IR radiation — the <u>temperature</u> of the food increases when it <u>absorbs</u> IR radiation, e.g. from a toaster's heating element.

7) <u>Electric heaters</u> heat a room in the same way. Electric heaters contain a <u>long piece of wire</u> that <u>heats up</u> when a current flows through it. This wire then <u>emits</u> lots of <u>infrared radiation</u> (and a little <u>visible light</u> — the wire <u>glows</u>). The emitted IR radiation is <u>absorbed</u> by objects and the air in the room — energy is transferred <u>by the IR waves</u> to the <u>thermal energy stores</u> of the objects, causing their <u>temperature</u> to <u>increase</u>.

Infrared Can Also Transfer Information

1) <u>Infrared</u> radiation can also be used to <u>transfer information</u>.

2) For example, it can be used to <u>send files</u> between <u>mobile phones</u> or <u>laptops</u>. The <u>distances</u> must be fairly <u>small</u> and the receiver must be in the <u>line of sight</u> of the emitter.

3) This is also how <u>TV remote controls</u> work. In fact, some <u>mobile phones</u> now have built in <u>software</u> which means that you can use your phone as a TV remote.

4) <u>Optical fibres</u> are thin <u>glass or plastic fibres</u> that can <u>carry data</u> (e.g. from telephones or computers) over long distances as <u>pulses</u> of <u>infrared</u> radiation. They usually use a <u>single</u> wavelength to prevent <u>dispersion</u> (p.34), which can otherwise cause some information to be <u>lost</u>.

5) They use <u>total internal reflection</u> (p.38) to send lots of data over <u>long distances</u>.

Revision time — adjust depending on brain wattage...

The next time you're feeling hungry and zap some food in the microwave, think of it as doing revision.

Q1   Give three uses of infrared radiation.   [3 marks]

More Uses of EM Waves

And we're still not finished with <u>uses</u> of <u>waves</u> — is there no end to their talents...

Photography Uses Visible Light

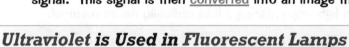

1) <u>Visible light</u> is the light that we can <u>see</u>. So it's only natural that we use it for <u>illuminating</u> things so that we can see them.

2) <u>Photographic film</u> reacts to light to form an image. This is how traditional <u>cameras</u> create <u>photographs</u>.

3) <u>Digital cameras</u> contain <u>image sensors</u>, which detect <u>visible light</u> and generate an electrical signal. This signal is then <u>converted</u> into an image that can be stored digitally or <u>printed</u>.

Ultraviolet is Used in Fluorescent Lamps

1) <u>Fluorescence</u> is a property of certain chemicals, where <u>ultraviolet</u> (<u>UV</u>) radiation is <u>absorbed</u> and then <u>visible light</u> is <u>emitted</u>. That's why fluorescent colours look so <u>bright</u> — they actually <u>emit light</u>.

2) <u>Fluorescent lights</u> use UV to <u>emit</u> visible light. They're <u>energy-efficient</u> (p.26) so they're good to use when light is needed for <u>long periods</u> (like in your <u>classroom</u>).

3) <u>Security pens</u> can be used to <u>mark</u> property (e.g. laptops). Under <u>UV light</u> the ink will <u>glow</u>, but it's <u>invisible</u> otherwise, helping to <u>identify</u> stolen property.

4) <u>Bank notes</u> and <u>passports</u> use a similar technique to detect <u>forgeries</u> — genuine notes and passports have <u>special markings</u> that only show up under UV light.

5) Ultraviolet radiation is sometimes used to <u>sterilise water</u>. It <u>kills bacteria</u> in the water, making it <u>safe</u> to drink. (Gamma rays are used in a similar way, see below.)

X-rays Let Us See Inside Things

1) <u>X-rays</u> can be used to view the <u>internal structure</u> of <u>objects</u> and <u>materials</u>, including our <u>bodies</u>.

2) They affect <u>photographic</u> film in the same way as <u>light</u>, meaning you can take <u>X-ray photographs</u>. But X-ray images are usually formed <u>electronically</u> these days.

3) <u>Radiographers</u> in <u>hospitals</u> take <u>X-ray images</u> to help doctors diagnose <u>broken bones</u> — X-rays are <u>transmitted by flesh</u> but are <u>absorbed</u> by <u>denser material</u> like <u>bones</u> or metal.

4) To produce an <u>X-ray image</u>, X-ray radiation is directed <u>through the object</u> or <u>body</u> onto a <u>detector plate</u>. The <u>brighter bits</u> of the image are where <u>fewer</u> <u>X-rays</u> get through, producing a <u>negative image</u> (the plate starts off <u>all white</u>).

5) X-rays are also used in <u>airport security scanners</u> to detect hidden objects that can't be detected with <u>metal detectors</u>.

Gamma Rays are Used for Sterilising Things

1) <u>Gamma rays</u> are used to <u>sterilise</u> medical instruments — they <u>kill</u> microbes (e.g. bacteria).

2) <u>Food</u> can be <u>sterilised</u> in the same way — again <u>killing microbes</u>. This keeps the food <u>fresh for longer</u>, without having to freeze it, cook it or preserve it some other way, and it's <u>perfectly safe</u> to eat.

3) Some <u>medical imaging</u> techniques such as <u>tracers</u> (p.55) use gamma rays to <u>detect cancer</u>.

4) Gamma radiation is also used in <u>cancer treatments</u> (p.56) — radiation is targeted at cancer cells to <u>kill them</u>. Doctors have to be careful to <u>minimise</u> the damage to <u>healthy cells</u> when treating cancer like this.

Don't lie to an X-ray — they can see right through you...

I hate to say it, but go back to page 45 and re-read all of the uses for electromagnetic waves to really learn them.

Q1   State two uses of ultraviolet radiation.   [2 marks]

Q2   Suggest one advantage of sterilising food with gamma rays.   [1 mark]

Revision Questions for Section 2

Wave goodbye to <u>Section 2</u> — you've finally reached the end. Now see how much you've learnt.
- Try these questions and <u>tick off each one</u> when you <u>get it right</u>.
- When you've done <u>all the questions</u> for a topic and are <u>completely happy</u> with it, tick off the topic.

<u>Wave Properties (p.32-34)</u> ☑

1) What is the amplitude, wavelength, frequency and period of a wave? ☑
2) Describe the difference between transverse and longitudinal waves and give an example of each kind. ☑
3) Describe experiments you could do to measure the speed of sound and the speed of ripples in water. ☑
4) Explain refraction and draw a ray diagram for a light ray entering a less optically dense material. ☑

<u>Sound and Exploring Structures with Waves (p.35-37)</u> ☑

5) What affects an object's ability to transmit given frequencies of sound? ☑
6) What is the frequency of ultrasound? ☑
7) Explain how ultrasound is used in industrial imaging and echo sounding. ☑
8) What is the frequency of infrasound? ☑
9) Describe how S-waves and P-waves can be used to explore the structure of the Earth's core. ☑

<u>Reflection and Refraction (p.38-39)</u> ☑

10) True or false? The angle of incidence always equals the angle of reflection for reflected waves. ☑
11) Draw a ray diagram for a light ray being reflected, where the angle of incidence is 25°. ☑
12) What conditions are needed for total internal reflection to occur? ☑
13) Define specular and diffuse reflection. ☑
14) Explain why you need to conduct experiments to investigate refraction in a dim room. ☑

<u>Visible Light and Colour (p.40)</u> ☑

15) True or false? Opaque objects transmit light. ☑
16) Explain what happens to white light that hits a white object. ☑
17) Describe how colour filters work. ☑

<u>Lenses (p.41-42)</u> ☑

18) Explain the terms 'real image' and 'virtual image'. ☑
19) Explain how a lens' curvature affects its power. ☑
20) Draw the ray diagram symbols for a converging lens and a diverging lens. ☑
21) True or false? Diverging lenses always produce real images. ☑

<u>Uses and Dangers of Electromagnetic Waves (p.43-47)</u> ☑

22) True or false? All electromagnetic waves are transverse. ☑
23) Give one potential danger of: a) ultraviolet radiation   b) X-rays and gamma rays. ☑
24) Describe the average power absorption and radiation for an object at a constant temperature. ☑
25) Explain how absorption, reflection and emission of radiation affects the Earth's temperature. ☑
26) Describe an experiment you could do to investigate how different materials radiate energy. ☑
27) What kind of current is used to generate radio waves in an antenna? ☑
28) What type of radiation is used in thermal imaging cameras? ☑
29) Give two uses of gamma rays. ☑

Section 2 — Waves and the Electromagnetic Spectrum

The Model of the Atom

We used to think <u>atoms</u> were tiny solid spheres (like ball-bearings), but they're <u>much more complex</u> than that...

The Theory of Atomic Structure Has Changed Over Time

1) In 1897 <u>J. J. Thomson</u> discovered that <u>electrons</u> could be <u>removed</u> from atoms, so atoms must be made up of smaller bits. He suggested the <u>'plum-pudding' model</u> — that atoms were <u>spheres of positive charge</u> with tiny negative electrons <u>stuck in them</u> like fruit in a plum pudding.

2) That "plum pudding" theory didn't last very long though. In 1909, <u>Rutherford</u> and <u>Marsden</u> tried firing a beam of <u>alpha particles</u> (see p.51) at <u>thin gold foil</u>. From the plum-pudding model, they expected the particles to <u>pass straight through</u> the gold sheet, or only be <u>slightly deflected</u>.

3) But although most of the particles did go <u>straight through</u> the sheet, some were deflected more than they had expected, and a few were <u>deflected back</u> the way they had come — something the plum-pudding model <u>couldn't explain</u>.

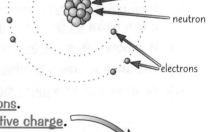

4) Being a pretty clued-up guy, Rutherford realised this meant that <u>most of the mass</u> of the atom was concentrated at the <u>centre</u> in a <u>tiny nucleus</u>.

5) He also realised that most of an atom is just <u>empty space</u>, and that the nucleus must have a <u>positive charge</u>, since it repelled the positive alpha particles.

6) This led to the creation of the <u>nuclear model</u> of the atom.

7) <u>Niels Bohr</u> tweaked Rutherford's idea a few years later by proposing a model where the electrons were in <u>fixed orbits</u> at <u>set distances</u> from the nucleus. These distances were called <u>energy levels</u> (p.50).

8) He suggested that electrons can <u>only</u> exist in these fixed orbits (or <u>shells</u>), and not anywhere inbetween.

9) This model is known as the <u>Bohr model</u> and is <u>pretty close</u> to our currently accepted model of the atom.

The Current Model of the Atom — Protons, Neutrons and Electrons

The quantities to do with atoms are <u>really tiny</u>, so they're written in <u>standard form</u>:

$$A \times 10^n$$

where A is a number between 1 and 10 and n is the number of places the decimal point would move if you wrote the number out in decimal form.

According to our current model of the atom:

1) An atom is a <u>positively-charged nucleus</u> surrounded by <u>negatively-charged electrons</u>.

2) Virtually all the <u>mass</u> of the atom is in the <u>nucleus</u>. The nucleus is <u>tiny</u> — about <u>10 000</u> times <u>smaller</u> than the whole atom. It contains <u>protons</u> (which are <u>positively charged</u>) and <u>neutrons</u> (which are <u>neutral</u>). The rest of the atom is mostly <u>empty space</u>.

3) The <u>negative electrons</u> whizz round outside the nucleus in <u>fixed orbits</u> called <u>energy levels</u> or <u>shells</u>. They give the atom its <u>overall size</u> of around 1×10^{-10} m.

4) Atoms are <u>neutral</u>, so <u>the number of protons = the number of electrons</u>. This is because <u>protons</u> and <u>electrons</u> have an <u>equal</u> but <u>opposite relative charge</u>.

5) If an atom <u>loses an electron</u> it becomes a <u>positive ion</u>. If it <u>gains</u> an electron it becomes a <u>negative ion</u> (p.50).

6) Atoms can <u>join together</u> to form <u>molecules</u> — e.g. molecules of <u>oxygen</u> gas are made up of two oxygen atoms bonded together. <u>Small molecules</u> like this have a typical size of 10^{-10} m — the <u>same sort of scale</u> as the size of an atom.

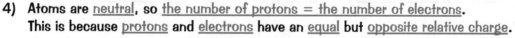

Particle	Relative Mass	Relative Charge
Proton	1	+1
Neutron	1	0
Electron	0.0005	−1

These models don't have anything on my miniature trains...

That's a whole lot of history, considering this is a book about physics. It's all good, educational fun though.

Q1   a) Describe the current model of the atom.   [4 marks]
      b) Describe how the radius of an atom compares to the size of its nucleus.   [1 mark]

Electron Energy Levels

There's some <u>quirky</u> stuff on this page — and the best part is that you can tell everyone you've been doing a little <u>quantum physics</u> today. Honestly. And if you study physics to a higher level, things get even <u>quirkier</u>.

Electrons *Can be* Excited *to Higher Energy Levels*

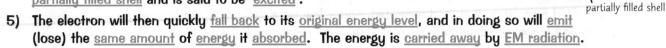

1) <u>Electrons</u> in an atom sit in <u>different energy levels</u> or shells.

2) Each <u>energy level</u> is a different distance from the <u>nucleus</u>.

3) An inner electron can <u>move up</u> to a higher energy level if it <u>absorbs electromagnetic (EM) radiation</u> with the right amount of <u>energy</u>.

4) When it does move up, it moves to an <u>empty</u> or <u>partially filled shell</u> and is said to be 'excited'.

5) The electron will then quickly <u>fall back</u> to its <u>original energy level</u>, and in doing so will <u>emit</u> (lose) the <u>same amount</u> of <u>energy</u> it <u>absorbed</u>. The energy is <u>carried away</u> by <u>EM radiation</u>.

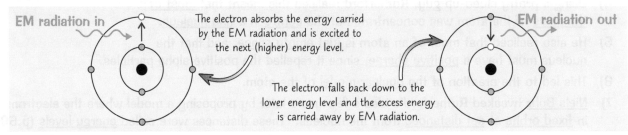

The electron absorbs the energy carried by the EM radiation and is excited to the next (higher) energy level.

The electron falls back down to the lower energy level and the excess energy is carried away by EM radiation.

6) The part of the <u>EM spectrum</u> the radiation <u>emitted from the atom</u> is from depends on its <u>energy</u>. This depends on <u>the energy levels</u> the electron moves between. A <u>higher energy</u> means a <u>higher frequency</u> of EM radiation — p.43. Often, <u>visible light</u> is released when electrons move between energy levels.

7) As you move <u>further out</u> from the nucleus, the energy levels get <u>closer together</u> (so the <u>difference in energy</u> between two levels <u>next to</u> each other gets <u>smaller</u>).

8) This means that an <u>excited</u> electron <u>falling</u> from the <u>third</u> energy level to the <u>second</u> would release <u>less energy</u> than an excited electron falling from the <u>second</u> energy level to the <u>first</u>. So the <u>frequency</u> of the generated radiation <u>decreases</u> as you get <u>further</u> from the <u>nucleus</u>.

9) Changes <u>within the nucleus itself</u> lead to the production of high energy, high frequency <u>gamma rays</u> (p.51).

An Atom *is Ionised if it Loses* an Electron

I can't see anything — are you positive you've lost one?

1) If an <u>outer electron</u> absorbs radiation with <u>enough energy</u>, it can move <u>so far</u> that it <u>leaves the atom</u>.

2) It is now a <u>free electron</u> and the atom is said to have been <u>ionised</u>.

3) The atom is now a <u>positive ion</u>. It's <u>positive</u> because there are now <u>more protons</u> than <u>electrons</u>.

4) An atom can lose <u>more than one electron</u>. The <u>more</u> electrons it loses, the <u>greater</u> its positive charge.

Nuclear Radiation *Ionises Atoms*

1) <u>Ionising radiation</u> is <u>any radiation</u> that can knock electrons from atoms.

2) <u>How likely</u> it is that each type of radiation will ionise an atom <u>varies</u>. You can see more about the <u>different types</u> of ionising nuclear radiation on the next page.

Ionising radiation — good for getting creases out of your clothes...

So, an electron absorbs EM radiation and moves up one or more energy levels, then falls back to its original energy level and loses the same amount of energy it absorbed, which is carried away by EM radiation. Simple...

Q1   What is a positive ion and how is one formed?   [2 marks]

Isotopes and Nuclear Radiation

Isotopes and ionisation. They sound similar, but they're totally different, so read this page carefully.

Isotopes are Different Forms of the Same Element

1) Each element has a set number of protons (so each nucleus has a given positive charge). The number of protons in an atom is called its atomic number or its proton number.

2) The mass (nucleon) number of an atom (the mass of the nucleus) is the number of protons + the number of neutrons in its nucleus.

3) Elements (usually isotopes) can be written as, e.g. carbon-14. This means that the mass number is 14.

4) Isotopes of an element are atoms with the same number of protons (the same atomic number) but a different number of neutrons (a different mass number). E.g. $^{18}_{8}O$ and $^{16}_{8}O$ are two isotopes of oxygen.

5) All elements have different isotopes, but there are usually only one or two stable ones.

6) The other unstable isotopes tend to decay into other elements and give out radiation as they try to become more stable. This process is called radioactive decay.

7) Radioactive substances spit out one or more types of ionising radiation when they decay: alpha, beta, gamma. They can also emit neutrons (n).

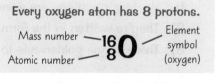

Every oxygen atom has 8 protons.

Mass number —$^{16}_{8}O$— Element symbol (oxygen)
Atomic number —

$^{14}_{\ 7}N$

Alpha Particles are Helium Nuclei

1) Alpha radiation is when an alpha particle (α) is emitted from the nucleus. An α-particle is two neutrons and two protons (like a helium nucleus).

2) They don't penetrate very far into materials and are stopped quickly — they can only travel a few cm in air and are absorbed by a thin sheet of paper.

3) Because of their size they are strongly ionising.

Beta Particles can be Electrons or Positrons

1) A beta-minus particle (β^-) is simply a fast-moving electron released by the nucleus. Beta-minus particles have virtually no mass and a relative charge of –1.

2) A beta-plus particle (β^+) is a fast-moving positron. The positron is the antiparticle of the electron. This just means it has exactly the same mass as the electron, but a positive (+1) charge.

3) They are both moderately ionising. Beta-minus particles have a range in air of a few metres and are absorbed by a sheet of aluminium (around 5 mm thick).

4) Positrons have a smaller range, because when they hit an electron the two destroy each other and produce gamma rays — this is called annihilation and it's used in PET scanning (see p.56).

Gamma Rays are EM Waves with a Short Wavelength

1) After a nucleus has decayed, it often undergoes nuclear rearrangement and releases some energy. Gamma rays (γ) are waves of EM radiation (p.43) released by the nucleus that carry away this energy.

2) They penetrate far into materials without being stopped and will travel a long distance through air.

3) This means they are weakly ionising because they tend to pass through rather than collide with atoms. Eventually they hit something and do damage.

4) They can be absorbed by thick sheets of lead or metres of concrete.

Isotopes of an outfit — same dress, different accessories...

Knowing different kinds of radiation and what can absorb them could bag you a few easy marks in an exam.

Q1   For each of alpha, beta-minus and gamma radiations, give an example of a material that could be used to absorb it. Refer to the material's thickness in your answer.   [3 marks]

Nuclear Equations

Nuclear equations show radioactive decay and once you get the hang of them they're dead easy. Get going.

Mass and Atomic Numbers Have to Balance

1) Nuclear equations are a way of showing radioactive decay by using element symbols (p.51).
2) They're written in the form: atom before decay → atom after decay + radiation emitted.
3) There is one golden rule to remember: the total mass and atomic numbers must be equal on both sides.

Alpha Decay Decreases the Charge and Mass of the Nucleus

When a nucleus emits an alpha particle, it loses two protons and two neutrons, so:

- the mass number decreases by 4.
- the atomic number decreases by 2.

$$_{88}^{226}\text{Ra} \rightarrow {}_{86}^{222}\text{Rn} + {}_{2}^{4}\alpha$$

| mass number: | 226 | → | 222 | + | 4 | (= 226) |
| atomic number: | 88 | → | 86 | + | 2 | (= 88) |

In both alpha and beta emissions, a new element will be formed, as the number of protons (atomic number) changes.

Beta-minus Decay Increases the Charge of the Nucleus

In a beta-minus decay, a neutron changes into a proton and an electron, so:

- the mass number doesn't change — as it has lost a neutron but gained a proton.
- the atomic number increases by 1 — because it has one more proton.

$$_{6}^{14}\text{C} \rightarrow {}_{7}^{14}\text{N} + {}_{-1}^{0}\beta$$

| mass number: | 14 | → | 14 | + | 0 | (= 14) |
| atomic number: | 6 | → | 7 | + | (–1) | (= 6) |

Positron Emission Decreases the Charge of the Nucleus

In beta-plus decay, a proton changes into a neutron and a positron, so:

- the mass number doesn't change — as it has lost a proton but gained a neutron.
- the atomic number decreases by 1 — because it has one less proton.

$$_{9}^{18}\text{F} \rightarrow {}_{8}^{18}\text{O} + {}_{1}^{0}\beta$$

| mass number: | 18 | → | 18 | + | 0 | (= 18) |
| atomic number: | 9 | → | 8 | + | 1 | (= 9) |

Neutron Emission Decreases the Mass of the Nucleus

When a nucleus emits a neutron:

- the mass number decreases by 1 — as it has lost a neutron.
- the atomic number stays the same.

$$_{4}^{13}\text{Be} \rightarrow {}_{4}^{12}\text{Be} + {}_{0}^{1}\text{n}$$

| mass number: | 13 | → | 12 | + | 1 | (= 13) |
| atomic number: | 4 | → | 4 | + | 0 | (= 4) |

Gamma Rays Don't Change the Charge or Mass of the Nucleus

1) Gamma rays (γ) are a way of getting rid of excess energy from an atom. The nucleus goes from an excited state to a more stable state by emitting a gamma ray.
2) The mass and atomic numbers stay the same after a gamma ray has been emitted.

Keep balanced during revision and practise nuclear equations...

Nuclear equations are simple, but that doesn't mean you shouldn't practise them. Try these questions on for size.

Q1   What type of radiation is given off in this decay? $_{3}^{8}\text{Li} \rightarrow {}_{4}^{8}\text{Be}$ + radiation.   [1 mark]

Q2   Write the nuclear equation for $_{86}^{219}\text{Rn}$ decaying to polonium (Po) by emitting an alpha particle.   [3 marks]

Half-Life

How quickly unstable nuclei decay is measured using activity and half-life — two very important terms.

Radioactivity is a Totally Random Process

1) Radioactive sources contain radioactive isotopes that give out radiation from the nuclei of their atoms.

2) This process is entirely random. This means that if you have 1000 unstable nuclei, you can't say when any one of them is going to decay, or which one will decay next.

3) If there are lots of nuclei though, you can predict how many will have decayed in a given time based on the half-life of the source (see below). The rate at which a source decays is called its ACTIVITY. Activity is measured in becquerels, Bq. 1 Bq is 1 decay per second.

4) Activity can be measured with a Geiger-Müller tube, which clicks each time it detects radiation. The tube can be attached to a counter, which displays the number of clicks per second (the count-rate).

5) You can also detect radiation using photographic film. The more radiation the film's exposed to, the darker it becomes (just like when you expose it to light).

The Radioactivity of a Source Decreases Over Time

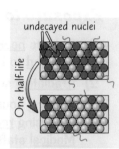
undecayed nuclei
One half-life

1) Each time a radioactive nucleus decays, one more radioactive nucleus disappears. As the unstable nuclei all steadily disappear, the activity as a whole will decrease.

2) For some isotopes it takes just a few hours before nearly all the unstable nuclei have decayed, whilst others last for millions of years.

3) The problem with trying to measure this is that the activity never reaches zero, so we have to use the idea of half-life to measure how quickly the activity drops off.

> The half-life is the average time taken for the number of radioactive nuclei in an isotope to halve.

4) A short half-life means the activity falls quickly, because the nuclei are very unstable and rapidly decay. Sources with a short half-life are dangerous because of the high amount of radiation they emit at the start, but they quickly become safe. (Half-life can also be described as the time taken for the activity to halve.)

5) A long half-life means the activity falls more slowly because most of the nuclei don't decay for a long time — the source just sits there, releasing small amounts of radiation for a long time. This can be dangerous because nearby areas are exposed to radiation for (millions of) years.

EXAMPLE: The activity of a radioactive sample is measured as 640 Bq. Two hours later it has fallen to 40 Bq. Find its half-life.

1) Count how many half-lives it took to fall to 40 Bq.

Initial activity:	after 1 half-life:	after 2 half-lives:	after 3 half-lives:	after 4 half-lives:
640	(÷2) → 320	(÷2) → 160	(÷2) → 80	(÷2) → 40

2) Calculate the half-life of the sample. Two hours is four half-lives — so the half-life is 2 hours ÷ 4 = **30 min**

You Can Measure Half-Life Using a Graph

1) If you plot a graph of activity against time (taking into account background radiation, p.54), it will always be shaped like the one to the right.

2) The half-life is found from the graph by finding the time interval on the bottom axis corresponding to a halving of the activity on the vertical axis. Easy.

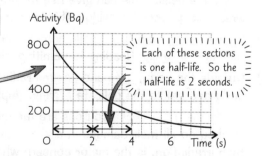

Each of these sections is one half-life. So the half-life is 2 seconds.

The half-life of a box of chocolates is about five minutes...

Half-life — the average time for the number of radioactive nuclei or the activity to halve. Simple.

Q1 A radioactive source has a half-life of 60 h and an activity of 480 Bq. Find its activity after 240 h. [2 marks]

Background Radiation and Contamination

Forget love — radiation is all around. Don't panic too much though, it's usually a pretty small amount.

Background Radiation Comes From Many Sources

Background radiation is the low-level radiation that's around us all the time. It comes from:

1) Radioactivity of naturally occurring unstable isotopes which are all around us — in the air, in some foods, building materials and some of the rocks under our feet.

2) Radiation from space, which is known as cosmic rays. These come mostly from the Sun. Luckily, the Earth's atmosphere protects us from much of this radiation.

3) Radiation due to human activity, e.g. fallout from nuclear explosions or nuclear waste. But this represents a tiny proportion of the total background radiation.

Coloured bits indicate more radiation from rocks

The amount of radiation you're exposed to (and so the amount of energy your body absorbs) is called the absorbed radiation dose. Your radiation dose varies depending on where you live or if you have a job that involves radiation.

Exposure to Radiation is called Irradiation

1) Objects near a radioactive source are irradiated by it. This simply means they're exposed to it (we're always being irradiated by background radiation sources).

2) Irradiating something does not make it radioactive (and won't turn you into a superhero).

3) Keeping sources in lead-lined boxes, standing behind barriers or being in a different room and using remote-controlled arms are all ways of reducing the effects of irradiation. Medical staff who work with radiation also wear photographic film badges to monitor their exposure.

Contamination is Radioactive Particles Getting onto Objects

1) If unwanted radioactive atoms get onto an object, the object is said to be contaminated. E.g. if you touch a radioactive source without wearing gloves, your hands would be contaminated.

2) These contaminating atoms might then decay, releasing radiation which could cause you harm.

3) Contamination is especially dangerous because radioactive particles could get inside your body.

4) Once a person is contaminated, they are at risk of harm until either the contamination is removed (which isn't always possible) or all the radioactive atoms have decayed.

5) Gloves and tongs should be used when handling sources, to avoid particles getting stuck to your skin or under your nails. Some industrial workers wear protective suits to stop them breathing in particles.

Radiation Damages Cells by Ionisation

1) Radiation can enter living cells and ionise atoms and molecules within them. This can lead to tissue damage.

2) Lower doses tend to cause minor damage without killing the cells. This can give rise to mutant cells which divide uncontrollably. This is cancer.

3) Higher doses tend to kill cells completely, causing radiation sickness (leading to vomiting, tiredness and hair loss) if a lot of cells all get blatted at once.

4) Outside the body, beta and gamma radiation are the most dangerous, because they can penetrate the body and get to the delicate organs. Alpha is less dangerous, because it can't penetrate the skin.

5) Inside the body, alpha sources are the most dangerous. Alpha particles are strongly ionising, so they do all their damage in a very localised area. That means contamination, rather than irradiation, is the major concern when working with alpha sources.

Background radiation — the ugly wallpaper of the Universe...

Make sure you can describe how to prevent irradiation and contamination, and why it's so important that you do.

Q1   Give three sources of background radiation.   [3 marks]

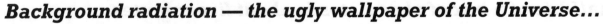

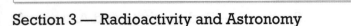

Uses of Radiation

Ionising radiation is very <u>dangerous</u> stuff, but used in the <u>right way</u> it can be incredibly useful.

The Hazards Associated with a Radioactive Source Depend on its Half-Life

1) The <u>lower</u> the <u>activity</u> (see p.53) of a <u>radioactive source</u>, the <u>safer</u> it is to be around.

2) If two sources that produce the <u>same type</u> of radiation start off with the <u>same activity</u>, the one with the <u>longer</u> half-life will be <u>more dangerous</u>. This is because, after <u>any period</u> of time, the activity of the source with a <u>short half-life</u> will have <u>fallen more</u> than the activity of the source with a <u>long half-life</u>.

3) If the two sources have <u>different initial activities</u>, the danger associated with them changes over time. Even if its <u>initial activity</u> is lower (so it is <u>initially safer</u>), the source with the <u>longer half-life</u> will be <u>more dangerous</u> after a certain period of time because its <u>activity</u> falls <u>more slowly</u>.

4) When choosing a radioactive source for an application, it's important to find a <u>balance</u> between a source that has the <u>right level of activity</u> for the right amount of <u>time</u>, and that isn't <u>too dangerous</u> for too long. <u>Careful planning</u> of <u>storage</u> and <u>disposal</u> of sources is needed, especially for sources with <u>long half-lives</u>.

Household Fire Alarms Use Alpha Radiation

1) A <u>weak</u> source of alpha radiation (p.51) is placed in a smoke detector, close to <u>two electrodes</u>.

2) The source causes <u>ionisation</u>, and a <u>current</u> of charged particles flows.

3) If there is a fire then smoke will <u>absorb</u> the charged particles — the current stops and the <u>alarm sounds</u>.

Food and Equipment can be Sterilised Using Gamma Rays

1) <u>Food</u> can be <u>irradiated with</u> (p.54) a <u>high dose</u> of <u>gamma rays</u> which will <u>kill</u> all <u>microbes</u>. This means that the food doesn't go bad as quickly as it would do otherwise.

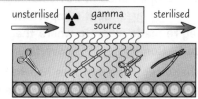

2) Similarly, <u>medical equipment</u> can be <u>sterilised</u> using gamma rays instead of being <u>boiled</u>.

3) <u>Irradiation</u> is a particularly good method of sterilisation because, unlike boiling, it doesn't involve <u>high temperatures</u>, so <u>fresh fruit</u> or <u>plastic instruments</u> can be totally <u>sterilised</u> without being <u>damaged</u>.

4) The radioactive source used for this needs to be a <u>very strong</u> emitter of <u>gamma rays</u> with a <u>reasonably long half-life</u> (at least several months) so that it doesn't need <u>replacing</u> too often.

Radiation is Used in Tracers and Thickness Gauges

1) Certain radioactive isotopes can be used as <u>tracers</u>. A <u>medical</u> tracer is <u>injected</u> into a patient (or <u>swallowed</u>) and its progress around the body is followed using an <u>external detector</u>. This method can be used to <u>detect</u> and <u>diagnose medical conditions</u> (e.g. cancer).

2) <u>All isotopes</u> which are taken <u>into the body</u> must be BETA or GAMMA emitters (never alpha), so that the radiation <u>passes out of the body</u> without doing too much damage. They should only last <u>a few hours</u>, so that the radioactivity inside the patient <u>quickly disappears</u> (i.e. they should have a <u>short half-life</u>).

3) <u>Gamma emitting tracers</u> are also used in <u>industry</u> to detect <u>leaks</u> in <u>underground pipes</u>.

4) <u>Beta radiation</u> is used in <u>thickness control</u>. You direct radiation through the stuff being made (e.g. paper), and put a detector on the other side, connected to a control unit. When the amount of <u>detected</u> radiation changes, it means the paper is coming out too thick or too thin, so the control unit adjusts the rollers to give the correct thickness.

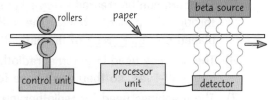

5) It needs to be a <u>beta</u> source, because then the paper will <u>partly block</u> the radiation (see p.51). If it <u>all</u> goes through (or <u>none</u> of it does), then the reading <u>won't change</u> at all as the thickness changes.

High activity is dangerous? Time for a rest then...

But only a short one — then make sure you can describe why different types of radiation have different uses.

Q1   Explain why radioactive sources that emit alpha radiation are not used as medical tracers.   [2 marks]

PET Scanning and Radiotherapy

And the uses keep on coming — we use radiation in lots of medical treatments like radiotherapy.

PET Scanning Can Help Diagnose Illnesses

Positron emission tomography or PET scanning is a technique used to show tissue or organ function, and can be used to diagnose medical conditions. For example, it can identify active cancer tumours by showing metabolic activity in tissue. Cancer cells have a much higher metabolism than healthy cells because they're growing like mad. And here's how it all works — put your best brains in, 'cos this is detailed:

1) Inject the patient with a substance used by the body, e.g. glucose, containing a positron-emitting radioactive isotope with a short half-life so it acts as a tracer, e.g. ^{11}C, ^{13}N, ^{15}O or ^{18}F. Over an hour or so the tracer moves through the body to the organs.

2) Positrons emitted by the isotope meet electrons in an organ and annihilate (see page 51), emitting high-energy gamma rays in opposite directions that are detected. Detectors around the body detect each pair of gamma rays — the tumour will lie along the same path as each pair. By detecting at least three pairs, the location of the tumour can be accurately found by triangulation.

3) The distribution of radioactivity matches up with metabolic activity. This is because more of the radioactive glucose (or whatever) injected into the patient is taken up and used by cells that are doing more work (cells with an increased metabolism, in other words).

4) The isotopes used in PET scanning have short half-lives, so it's important that they're made close to where they'll be used. Some hospitals have their own cyclotron to make the isotopes on-site.

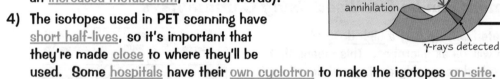

PET scanner
γ-rays
positron-electron annihilation
γ-rays detected

map of a 'slice' through patient's head showing concentration of radiotracer

5) Otherwise, if the isotopes had to be transported over a large distance, their activity could be too low by the time they arrived at the hospital, making them no longer as useful.

Radiation can be Used Internally or Externally to Treat Tumours

1) With internal radiation therapy, a radioactive material is placed inside the body into or near a tumour. This can be done in many ways, e.g. by injecting or implanting a small amount of radioactive substance.

2) Alpha emitters are usually injected near to the tumour. As alpha particles are strongly ionising, they do lots of damage to the nearby area (the cancerous cells), but the damage to normal tissue surrounding the tumour is limited because they have such a short range.

3) Beta emitters are often used in implants, placed inside or next to a tumour. Beta radiation is able to penetrate the casing of the implant (unlike alpha particles, which would be stopped) before damaging nearby cancerous cells. As they have a longer range than alpha particles, they can damage healthy cells further away from the cancerous cells.

4) The half-lives of the sources used for internal treatments are usually short, to limit the time that a radioactive substance is inside the patient's body.

5) Tumours can be treated externally using gamma rays aimed at the tumour, as these are able to penetrate through the patient's body. The radiation is carefully focused on the tumour, and sometimes shielding is placed on other areas of the patient's body, but some damage is still done to surrounding healthy cells.

6) The sources used in external radiotherapy treatments should have long half-lives, so they don't have to be replaced often.

7) The machines used for radiotherapy are often surrounded by shielding and kept in a designated room to reduce the risk to staff and patients in the hospital.

PET scanning — how they check prices at the pet shop...

That's a lot of stuff to get your head around. Re-read this page, have a quick tea break, then try this question.

Q1   Explain how a PET scan can detect a cancerous tumour in a patient.   [4 marks]

Nuclear Fission

It's amazing how much <u>energy</u> there is <u>trapped</u> in a little atom. This energy is released by <u>nuclear fission</u>.

Nuclear Fission — the Splitting Up of Big Atomic Nuclei

<u>Nuclear fission</u> is a type of <u>nuclear reaction</u> that is used to <u>release energy</u> from uranium (or plutonium) atoms, e.g. in a nuclear reactor. <u>Huge amounts</u> of energy can be released this way by using a <u>chain reaction</u>...

The Chain Reaction:

1) A <u>slow-moving neutron</u> is fired at a <u>large</u>, <u>unstable</u> nucleus — often uranium-235. The neutron is <u>absorbed</u> by the nucleus — this makes the atom more <u>unstable</u> and causes it to <u>split</u>.

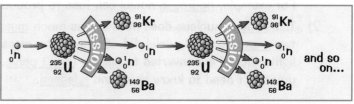

A neutron can be <u>absorbed</u> by the nucleus because it has <u>no charge</u> — i.e. it's not <u>repelled</u> by the positive charge of the nucleus.

2) When the U-235 atom splits it forms <u>two new lighter</u> elements ('<u>daughter nuclei</u>') and <u>energy</u> is released.

3) There are lots of different pairs of atoms that uranium can split into, e.g. krypton-91 and barium-143, but all these new nuclei are <u>radioactive</u>.

4) Each time a <u>uranium</u> atom <u>splits up</u>, it also spits out <u>two or three neutrons</u>, which can hit <u>other</u> uranium nuclei, causing them to <u>split</u> also, and so on and so on. This is a <u>chain reaction</u>.

Chain Reactions in Reactors Must be Carefully Controlled

1) The <u>neutrons</u> released by fission reactions in a nuclear reactor have <u>a lot</u> of energy.

2) These neutrons will only cause <u>other</u> nuclear fissions (and cause a chain reaction) if they are <u>moving slowly</u> enough to be <u>captured</u> by the uranium nuclei in the fuel rods. These <u>slow-moving</u> neutrons are called <u>thermal neutrons</u>.

3) To do this, the uranium <u>fuel rods</u> are placed in a <u>moderator</u> (for example, graphite) to <u>slow down</u> the fast-moving neutrons.

4) <u>Control rods</u>, often made of <u>boron</u>, limit the rate of fission by <u>absorbing</u> excess neutrons. They are placed <u>inbetween</u> the fuel rods and are <u>raised</u> and <u>lowered</u> into the reactor to <u>control</u> the chain reaction.

5) This creates a <u>steady rate</u> of nuclear fission, where <u>one new neutron</u> produces another fission.

6) If the chain reaction in a nuclear reactor is <u>left to continue unchecked</u>, large amounts of <u>energy</u> are <u>released</u> in a very <u>short time</u>. <u>Many new fissions</u> will follow each fission, causing a <u>runaway reaction</u> which could lead to an <u>explosion</u>.

Nuclear Power Stations are Really Glorified Steam Engines

1) Nuclear power stations are powered by <u>nuclear reactors</u> that create controlled chain reactions.

2) The <u>energy</u> released by <u>fission</u> is transferred to the <u>thermal</u> energy store of the <u>moderator</u>. This is then transferred to the <u>thermal</u> energy store of the <u>coolant</u>, and then to the <u>thermal energy store</u> of the <u>cold water</u> passing through the <u>boiler</u>. This causes the water to <u>boil</u> (p.94) and energy to be transferred to the <u>kinetic</u> energy store of the <u>steam</u>.

3) This energy is then <u>transferred</u> to the <u>kinetic</u> energy store of a <u>turbine</u> and then to the <u>kinetic</u> energy store of a <u>generator</u>. The energy is then <u>transferred away</u> from the generator <u>electrically</u>.

Revise nuclear power — full steam ahead...

Nuclear reactors are carefully-designed to release energy safely, but they still have issues (see next page).

Q1   Draw a diagram showing how fission can lead to a chain reaction.   [3 marks]

Nuclear Fusion and Nuclear Power

Loads of energy's released either when you break apart <u>really big nuclei</u> or join together <u>really small nuclei</u>. You can't do much with the ones in the middle, I'm afraid. But at least that's one less thing to learn...

Nuclear Fusion — Joining Small Nuclei

1) <u>Nuclear fusion</u> is the opposite of nuclear fission. In nuclear fusion, two <u>light nuclei collide</u> at high speed and <u>join</u> (fuse) to create a <u>larger</u>, heavier nucleus. For example, <u>hydrogen</u> nuclei can fuse to produce a <u>helium nucleus</u>.

2) This <u>heavier</u> nucleus does not have as much <u>mass</u> as the two <u>separate</u>, light nuclei did. Some of the mass of the lighter nuclei is converted to <u>energy</u> (<u>don't panic</u>, you don't need to know <u>how</u>) and <u>released</u>.

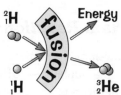

$^{2}_{1}H$ fusion   Energy

$^{1}_{1}H$ $^{3}_{2}He$

Fusion Only Happens at High Temperatures and Pressures

1) The <u>big problem</u> is that fusion only happens at <u>really high pressures and temperatures</u> (about <u>10 000 000 °C</u>). This is because the <u>positively charged</u> nuclei have to get <u>very close</u> to fuse, so the strong <u>force</u> due to <u>electrostatic repulsion</u> (p.82) has to be overcome.

2) It's <u>really hard</u> to create the <u>right conditions</u> for fusion. <u>No material</u> can withstand that kind of temperature — it would just be <u>vaporised</u>. So fusion reactors are <u>really hard</u> and <u>expensive</u> to try to build.

3) There are a few <u>experimental</u> reactors around at the moment, but none of them are generating electricity yet. It takes <u>more</u> power to get up to temperature than the reactor can produce.

> BEWARE: the filling of this fruit pie is hotter than the conditions needed for fusion.

Using Nuclear Power Has Its Pros and Cons

Nuclear power has a lot going for it, but some people are completely against it being used.

1) <u>Public perception</u> of nuclear power can be <u>very negative</u> — it's seen by many to be <u>very dangerous</u>.

2) Some people worry that nuclear waste can <u>never be disposed of safely</u>. The waste products from nuclear fission have <u>very long half-lives</u>, meaning they'll be <u>radioactive</u> for <u>hundreds</u> or <u>thousands</u> (even millions) of <u>years</u>. There is always a danger that they could <u>leak out</u> and <u>pollute</u> land, rivers and oceans.

3) <u>Nuclear power</u> also carries the risk of <u>leaks</u> directly from the power station or a <u>major catastrophe</u> like those at <u>Chernobyl</u> and <u>Fukushima</u>.

4) However, nuclear power is generally a <u>pretty safe</u> way of generating electricity — it's not as <u>risky</u> as <u>some people may think</u> it is.

5) And it's not all doom and gloom. Nuclear power is a <u>very reliable</u> energy resource and reduces the need for fossil fuels (which are already running out — see p.28).

6) <u>Fossil fuels</u> (coal, oil and gas) all release carbon dioxide (CO_2) when they're burnt. This adds to the <u>greenhouse effect</u> and <u>global warming</u>. Burning coal and oil also releases <u>sulfur dioxide</u> that can cause <u>acid rain</u>. Nuclear power <u>doesn't</u> release these gases, so in this way it is a very <u>clean</u> source of energy.

7) <u>Huge</u> amounts of energy can be generated from a relatively <u>small</u> amount of <u>nuclear material</u>. Nuclear <u>fuel</u> (i.e. the uranium) is <u>cheap</u> and <u>readily available</u>.

8) However, the <u>overall cost</u> of nuclear power is <u>high</u> due to the initial cost of the <u>power plant</u> and final <u>decommissioning</u> — dismantling a nuclear plant safely takes <u>decades</u>.

*Pity they can't release energy by confusion...**

Thankfully you don't need to know the complicated processes behind fission and fusion, you just need to have an idea of the steps in them. Remember that fusion is tricky because it needs high temperatures and pressures.

Q1   Explain why fusion only occurs at high temperatures and pressures.   [2 marks]

     *There'd be plenty of physics books to use as fuel.

The Solar System and Gravity

The <u>Sun</u> is the centre of the <u>Solar System</u>. It's <u>orbited</u> by <u>eight planets</u>, along with a bunch of other objects.

The Solar System has One Star — The Sun

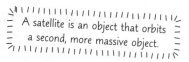
A satellite is an object that orbits a second, more massive object.

The <u>Solar System</u> is all the <u>stuff</u> that <u>orbits our Sun</u>. This includes things like:

1) <u>Planets</u> — these are large objects that <u>orbit a star</u>. The <u>eight</u> planets in our Solar System are, in order (from the Sun outwards): Mercury, Venus, Earth, Mars, Jupiter, Saturn, Uranus and Neptune.

2) <u>Dwarf planets</u>, like our pal Pluto. These are planet-like objects that <u>aren't big enough</u> to be planets.

3) <u>Moons</u> — these orbit <u>planets</u> with <u>almost circular</u> orbits. They're a type of <u>natural satellite</u> (i.e. they're not man-made).

4) <u>Artificial satellites</u> (ones humans have built) that usually orbit the <u>Earth</u> in fairly <u>circular orbits</u>.

5) <u>Asteroids</u> — lumps of <u>rock</u> and <u>metals</u> that orbit the <u>Sun</u>. They're usually found in the <u>asteroid belt</u>.

6) <u>Comets</u> — lumps of <u>ice</u> and <u>dust</u> that orbit the <u>Sun</u>. Their orbits are usually <u>highly elliptical</u> (a very stretched out circle) — some travel from near to the Sun to the <u>outskirts</u> of our <u>Solar System</u>.

Gravity Provides the Force That Creates Orbits

1) The planets move around the Sun in <u>almost circular</u> orbits (same goes for the Earth and the <u>Moon</u>).

2) You saw on p.17 that an object in a <u>circular</u> orbit at a <u>constant speed</u> is <u>constantly accelerating</u>.

3) The <u>force</u> causing this is the <u>centripetal</u> force. It acts towards the <u>centre</u> of the circle.

4) This force would cause the object to just <u>fall</u> towards whatever it was orbiting, but as the object is <u>already moving</u>, it just causes it to <u>change its direction</u>.

5) The object <u>keeps accelerating</u> towards what it's orbiting but the <u>instantaneous velocity</u> (which is at a <u>right angle</u> to the <u>acceleration</u>) keeps it travelling in a <u>circle</u>.

6) The force that makes this happen is provided by the <u>gravitational force</u> (gravity) between the <u>planet</u> and the Sun (or between the <u>planet</u> and its <u>satellites</u>).

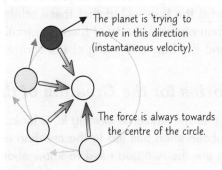
The planet is 'trying' to move in this direction (instantaneous velocity).

The force is always towards the centre of the circle.

The Force due to Gravity Depends on Mass and Distance

1) Back on page 17 you saw that the <u>weight</u> (i.e. the <u>force</u> on an object due to gravity) of any object varies depending on the <u>strength</u> (g) of the <u>gravitational field</u> that it is in.

2) <u>Gravitational field strength</u> depends on the <u>mass</u> of the body <u>creating</u> the field. The <u>larger</u> the mass of the body, the <u>stronger</u> its gravitational field. (The Earth is <u>more massive</u> than the Moon, so an object would <u>weigh more</u> on Earth than it would on the Moon.)

The fact that different planets orbit the Sun at different speeds means that the distances between planets vary over time.

3) Gravitational field strength also varies with <u>distance</u>. The <u>closer</u> you get to a star or planet, the <u>stronger</u> the <u>gravitational force</u> is.

4) The <u>stronger</u> the force, the <u>larger</u> the <u>instantaneous velocity</u> needed to <u>balance</u> it.

5) So the <u>closer</u> to a star or planet you get, the <u>faster</u> you need to go to remain in <u>orbit</u>.

6) For an object in a <u>stable orbit</u>, if the <u>speed</u> of the object <u>changes</u>, the <u>size</u> (<u>radius</u>) of its <u>orbit</u> must do so too. <u>Faster</u> moving objects will move in a <u>stable</u> orbit with a <u>smaller radius</u> than <u>slower</u> moving ones.

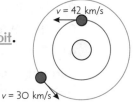
v = 42 km/s

v = 30 km/s

Revision's hard work — you've got to plan et...

Make sure you know what orbits what and how to tell a moon from a dwarf planet. Then get your head around all that stuff about orbits — it sounds a bit complicated, but it's really just about balancing forces.

Q1   Describe the orbits of: a) planets   b) moons   c) comets   [3 marks]

Changing Ideas about the Universe

Over time, we've come up with lots of ideas about how the Universe began and how our Solar System looks.

Ancient Greeks Thought the Earth was the Centre of the Solar System

There have been lots of different models of our Solar System:

1) Geocentric model — this theory suggested that the Sun, Moon, planets and stars all orbited the Earth in perfect circles. It arose because people on Earth didn't have telescopes and saw the Sun and Moon travelling across the sky in the same way every day and night. It was the accepted model of the Universe from the time of the ancient Greeks until the 1500s.

2) Next up was the heliocentric model (Sun at the centre of the Solar System). It said that the Earth and all of the planets orbited the Sun in perfect circles.

3) Galileo found one of the best pieces of evidence for this theory — the moons around Jupiter. Whilst looking at Jupiter with a telescope, he noticed some stars in a line near the planet. When he looked again, he saw these 'stars' never moved away from Jupiter and seemed to be carried along with the planet. This showed not everything was in orbit around the Earth — evidence that the geocentric model was wrong.

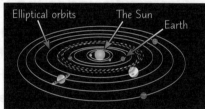

4) Gradually, evidence for the heliocentric model increased thanks to more technological advances.

5) The current model still says that the planets in our Solar System orbit the Sun — but that these orbits are actually elliptical rather than circular (we treat them as circular to make life easier though) and the Sun isn't really at the centre of the Universe.

Our current view of the Solar System.

Theories for the Creation of the Universe Have Also Changed Over Time

As big as the Universe already is, it looks like it's getting even bigger (it's expanding). This observation has led to the creation of numerous models that try to explain the creation of the Universe. These are the two you need to know about:

Steady State — Matter is Always Being Created

1) The 'Steady State' theory says that the Universe has always existed as it is now, and it always will do. It's based on the idea that the Universe appears pretty much the same everywhere.

2) As the Universe expands, new matter is constantly being created.

3) This means that the density (p.93) of the Universe is always roughly the same.

4) In this theory there is no beginning or end to the Universe.

The Big Bang — the Universe Started with an Explosion

1) Initially, all the matter in the Universe occupied a very small space.

2) This tiny space was very dense (p.93) and so was very hot.

3) Then it 'exploded' — space started expanding, and the expansion is still going on.

4) This theory gives a finite age for the Universe (around 13.8 billion years).

Currently, the Big Bang is the accepted theory of how the Universe began. This is based on evidence shown on the next page.

Forget the Sun, I'm pretty sure everything revolves around me...

Make sure you can describe each theory above and how it compares to our current ideas about the Universe.

Q1   Explain the difference between the geocentric and heliocentric models of the Solar System.   [1 mark]

Q2   Give two differences between the Steady State and Big Bang theories.   [2 marks]

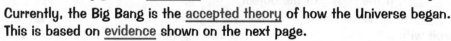

Red-shift and CMB Radiation

The <u>Big Bang model</u> is the <u>most convincing explanation</u> we've got for how the Universe started.

Red-shift Suggests the Universe is Expanding

Most <u>galaxies</u> seem to be <u>moving away</u> from each other.
There's good evidence for this:

1) Different elements <u>absorb</u> different <u>frequencies</u> (or wavelengths) of light.

2) Each element produces a <u>specific pattern</u> of <u>dark lines</u> at the frequencies that it <u>absorbs</u> in the visible part of the EM spectrum (p.43).

3) When we look at <u>light from distant galaxies</u> we see the <u>same patterns</u> but at <u>slightly lower frequencies</u> than they should be.

4) There's an <u>observed increase in the wavelength</u> of light coming from the galaxies and the patterns have been <u>shifted</u> towards the <u>red end</u> of the spectrum. This is called <u>red-shift</u>.

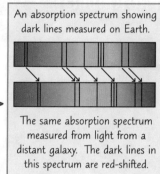

An absorption spectrum showing dark lines measured on Earth.

The same absorption spectrum measured from light from a distant galaxy. The dark lines in this spectrum are red-shifted.

<u>Red-shift</u> is the same effect as the vrrr-oom from a racing car or the sound of an ambulance as they drive past you. The noise sounds <u>lower-pitched</u> when it's travelling away from you because it drops in <u>frequency</u> (the <u>Doppler effect</u>).

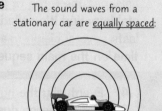

The sound waves from a stationary car are <u>equally spaced</u>:

But for a moving car, the wavelengths are <u>longer</u> here... ...than here.

So the frequency of the sound waves is <u>lower</u> if the car is moving <u>away</u> from you.

5) <u>Measurements</u> of the red-shift suggest that <u>all the distant galaxies</u> are <u>moving away from us</u> very quickly — and it's the <u>same result</u> whichever direction you look in.

6) <u>More distant</u> galaxies have <u>greater</u> red-shifts than nearer ones — they show a <u>bigger</u> observed <u>increase</u> in <u>wavelength</u>.

7) This means that more distant galaxies are <u>moving away faster</u> than nearer ones. This provides evidence that the whole Universe is <u>expanding</u>.

There's Microwave Radiation from All Directions

1) Scientists have detected <u>low frequency electromagnetic radiation</u> coming from <u>all parts</u> of the Universe.

2) This radiation is mainly in the <u>microwave</u> part of the EM spectrum. It's known as the <u>cosmic microwave background radiation</u> (CMB radiation).

Cosmic maaaaaan!

CMB radiation is Strong Evidence for the Big Bang

1) <u>Red-shift</u> can be explained by <u>both</u> the Steady State and Big Bang theories.

2) In both models, objects are <u>moving away</u> from the observer as the Universe expands, so red-shift would be observed for either model.

3) However, CMB radiation <u>only</u> supports the <u>Big Bang model</u> as it shows the Universe had a <u>beginning</u>.

4) This is why the <u>Big Bang theory</u> is currently our <u>accepted model</u> for the start of the Universe.

According to the Big Bang model, the CMB radiation is the leftover energy of the initial explosion.

My brain's shifted towards the tired end of the spectrum...

The Big Bang model is the best one we've got to explain how the Universe began, but it may need some tweaking in the future if we find new evidence it can't explain. Scientists, pfft, don't they ever finish anything?

Q1 What is red-shift? [1 mark]

Q2 What theory does CMB radiation support? [1 mark]

The Life Cycle of Stars

Stars go through <u>many traumatic stages</u> in their lives — just like teenagers.

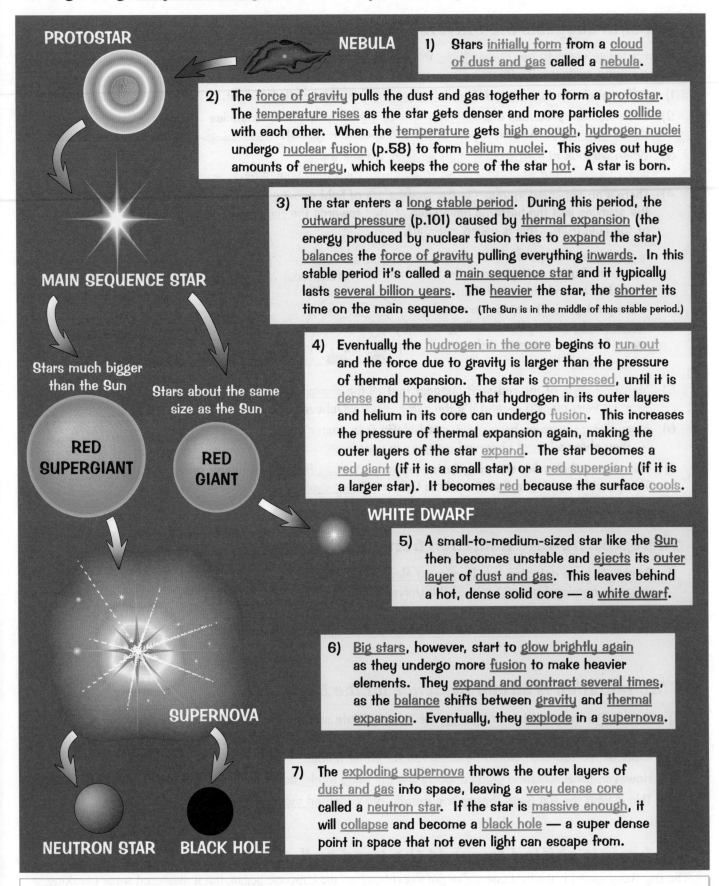

PROTOSTAR

NEBULA

1) Stars <u>initially form</u> from a <u>cloud of dust and gas</u> called a <u>nebula</u>.

2) The <u>force of gravity</u> pulls the dust and gas together to form a <u>protostar</u>. The <u>temperature rises</u> as the star gets denser and more particles <u>collide</u> with each other. When the <u>temperature</u> gets <u>high enough</u>, <u>hydrogen nuclei</u> undergo <u>nuclear fusion</u> (p.58) to form <u>helium nuclei</u>. This gives out huge amounts of <u>energy</u>, which keeps the <u>core</u> of the star <u>hot</u>. A star is born.

MAIN SEQUENCE STAR

3) The star enters a <u>long stable period</u>. During this period, the <u>outward pressure</u> (p.101) caused by <u>thermal expansion</u> (the energy produced by nuclear fusion tries to <u>expand</u> the star) <u>balances</u> the <u>force of gravity</u> pulling everything <u>inwards</u>. In this stable period it's called a <u>main sequence star</u> and it typically lasts <u>several billion years</u>. The <u>heavier</u> the star, the <u>shorter</u> its time on the main sequence. (The Sun is in the middle of this stable period.)

Stars much bigger than the Sun

Stars about the same size as the Sun

4) Eventually the <u>hydrogen in the core</u> begins to <u>run out</u> and the force due to gravity is larger than the pressure of thermal expansion. The star is <u>compressed</u>, until it is <u>dense</u> and <u>hot</u> enough that hydrogen in its outer layers and helium in its core can undergo <u>fusion</u>. This increases the pressure of thermal expansion again, making the outer layers of the star <u>expand</u>. The star becomes a <u>red giant</u> (if it is a small star) or a <u>red supergiant</u> (if it is a larger star). It becomes <u>red</u> because the surface <u>cools</u>.

RED SUPERGIANT

RED GIANT

WHITE DWARF

5) A small-to-medium-sized star like the <u>Sun</u> then becomes unstable and <u>ejects</u> its <u>outer layer</u> of <u>dust and gas</u>. This leaves behind a hot, dense solid core — a <u>white dwarf</u>.

6) <u>Big stars</u>, however, start to <u>glow brightly again</u> as they undergo more <u>fusion</u> to make heavier elements. They <u>expand and contract several times</u>, as the <u>balance</u> shifts between <u>gravity</u> and <u>thermal expansion</u>. Eventually, they <u>explode</u> in a <u>supernova</u>.

SUPERNOVA

7) The <u>exploding supernova</u> throws the outer layers of <u>dust and gas</u> into space, leaving a <u>very dense core</u> called a <u>neutron star</u>. If the star is <u>massive enough</u>, it will <u>collapse</u> and become a <u>black hole</u> — a super dense point in space that not even light can escape from.

NEUTRON STAR   **BLACK HOLE**

It's the beginning of the world as we know it...

Pretty neat, seeing how stars like our Sun — which all of us rely on — were made all those years ago.

Q1   Describe the life cycle of a star much larger than our Sun, beginning from a nebula.   [6 marks]

Looking Into Space

There are various objects in space, and they emit or reflect different frequencies of EM radiation. And that can be really useful to help us find out what's going on 'out there'.

Telescopes are Used to Observe the Universe

Telescopes help you to see distant objects clearly. There are loads of different kinds (see below) and they all work in different ways. The one you're most likely to have seen is an optical telescope — ones that detect visible light.

Telescopes use refraction (p.34) and reflection (p.38) to allow you to see distant objects. You need to know how to improve the quality of the image you can see using them:

1) Increase the aperture of the telescope. This is the diameter of the objective lens — the big lens at the end of the telescope where light from the distant object enters the telescope.

2) Use a higher quality objective lens.

Space Telescopes Have a Clearer View Than Those on Earth

1) If you're trying to detect light, Earth's atmosphere gets in the way — it absorbs a lot of the light coming from space before it can reach us. To observe the frequencies absorbed, you have to go above the atmosphere.

2) Then there's pollution. Light pollution (light thrown up into the sky from street lamps, etc.) makes it hard to pick out dim objects. And air pollution can reflect and absorb light coming from space.

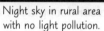

Night sky in rural area with no light pollution. Night sky in urban area with light pollution.

3) So to get the best view possible from Earth, a telescope should be on top of a mountain (where there's less atmosphere above it), and in a dark place away from cities (e.g. on Hawaii).

4) To avoid the problem of the atmosphere completely, you can put your telescope in space.

Different Telescopes Detect Different Types of EM Wave

To get as full a picture of the Universe as possible, you need to detect different kinds of EM wave.

1) The earliest telescopes were all optical telescopes. They're used to look at objects close by and in other galaxies. But many objects in the Universe aren't detectable using visible light — so other types of EM telescopes are needed to observe them.

2) From the 1940s onwards, telescopes were developed for all parts of the EM spectrum. These modern telescopes mean we can now 'see' parts of the Universe that we couldn't see before and learn more about the Universe, e.g. its structure.

3) X-ray telescopes are a good way to 'see' violent, high-temperature events in space, like exploding stars.

4) Radio telescopes were responsible for the discovery of the cosmic microwave background radiation (p.61) — this helped scientists to learn more about the origins of the Universe.

5) Telescopes are improving all the time — bigger telescopes give us better resolution (i.e. a lot of detail) and can gather more light, so we can see things we couldn't before as they were too faint. Improved magnification means we can now look further into space — more and more galaxies are being discovered.

6) Modern telescopes often work alongside computers. Computers help create clearer and sharper images and make it easy to capture these pictures so they can be analysed later.

7) Computers make it possible to collect and store huge amounts of data, 24 hours a day, without having to rely on humans. They also make it easier and quicker to analyse all this data.

Now you've got an excuse to stare into space during lessons...

Although you won't see much without a telescope. You need to be able to explain different ways of improving images from telescopes — remember, high up and in a dark place is good, and sticking one in space is even better.

Q1 Give three ways of improving the image you can see through a telescope on Earth. [3 marks]

Revision Questions for Section 3

And that's <u>Section 3</u> over and done with — time to celebrate with some fun revision questions (woo...).
- Try these questions and <u>tick off each one</u> when you <u>get it right</u>.
- When you've done <u>all the questions</u> for a topic and are <u>completely happy</u> with it, tick off the topic.

<u>Atoms (p.49-50)</u> ☑

1) Briefly explain how the model of the atom has changed over time.
2) True or false? Atoms are neutral.
3) What happens to an electron in an atom if it releases EM radiation?
4) True or false? The frequency of generated radiation increases as the site of generation gets closer to the nucleus.

<u>Radioactivity (p.51-58)</u> ☑

5) What is the atomic number of an atom?
6) What is an isotope? Are they usually stable?
7) Name four things that may be emitted during radioactive decay.
8) For the four types of ionising radiation, give: a) their ionising power,   b) their range in air.
9) Explain why alpha radiation could not be used to check the thickness of metal sheets.
10) Describe how the mass and atomic numbers of an atom change if it emits an alpha particle.
11) In what type of nuclear decay does a neutron change into a proton within the nucleus?
12) What type of nuclear decay doesn't change the mass or charge of the nucleus?
13) What is the activity of a radioactive source? What are its units?
14) Define half-life.
15) True or false? A short half-life means a small proportion of the atoms are decaying per second.
16) What is background radiation?
17) Give three uses of radiation.
18) True or false? Radioactive sources used in PET scans have a long half-life.
19) Briefly describe how a fission reaction occurs.
20) True or false? The fission products of uranium-235 are also radioactive.
21) Explain the function of control rods in a fission reactor.
22) State the conditions needed to create a fusion reaction.

<u>Astronomy (p.59-63)</u> ☑

23) Name the eight planets in our Solar System.
24) What do asteroids orbit?
25) Name the force that keeps objects in orbit.
26) Explain how our ideas about our Solar System have changed over time.
27) Compare the Steady State and Big Bang theories. Which is the currently accepted theory?
28) What does CMB radiation stand for?
29) Explain how both the Steady State and Big Bang theories can account for red-shift.
30) List the life cycle stages that a star the size of our Sun goes through.
31) Explain why placing a telescope away from nearby cities improves the images it produces.

Energy Transfers and Systems

Re-read pages 24 and 25. You'll need to remember everything on those pages for this section. It could come up in the exam.

When a System Changes, Energy is Transferred

1) A system is just a fancy word for a single object (e.g. the air in a piston) or a group of objects (e.g. two colliding vehicles) that you're interested in. You can define your system to be anything you like.

2) When a system changes, energy is transferred (p.25). It can be transferred into or away from the system, between different objects in the system or between different types of energy stores.

3) Whenever a system changes, some energy is dissipated and stored in less useful ways (p.26).

4) The efficiency of a transfer is the proportion of the total energy supplied that ends up in useful energy stores (p. 26).

5) You can use diagrams to show how efficient a transfer is, and which stores the energy is transferred to (see p.25 and 27).

6) How you define your system changes how you describe the energy transfers that take place (see below). A closed system is one that's defined so that the net change in energy is zero (p.25).

Energy can be Transferred by Heating...

1) A pan of water is heated on a gas camping stove.

2) When the system is the pan of water, energy is transferred into the system by heating to the thermal energy stores of the pan and the water, which increases their temperature.

3) When the system is the camping stove and the pan, energy is transferred from the chemical energy store of the gas to the thermal energy stores of the pan and the water, increasing their temperature.

...by Forces Doing Work...

1) A box is lifted up off of the floor. The box is the system.

2) As the box is lifted, work is done (see next page) against gravity.

3) This causes energy to be transferred to the box's kinetic and gravitational potential energy stores.

If the box was dropped, the gravitational force would do work to transfer energy from the box's GPE store to its kinetic energy store.

...or by Electrical Equipment

1) Electrical devices work by transferring energy between different energy stores.

2) For example, electric irons transfer energy electrically from the mains power supply to the thermal energy store of their metal plates.

You can show energy transfers using diagrams — see p.25.

1) An electric toothbrush is a system. It transfers energy electrically from the chemical energy store of its battery to the kinetic energy store of its bristles.

2) Some of this energy is transferred out of the system to the surroundings by sound and by heating.

1) A hair dryer is a system. It transfers energy into the system electrically from the mains supply to the kinetic energy store of the fan inside of it.

2) It also transfers energy electrically to the thermal energy store of the heating element and some energy is transferred away by sound.

All this work, I can feel my energy stores being drained...

Make sure you understand exactly what a system contains before you describe any energy transfers.

Q1   Describe the energy transfers that occur when the wind causes a windmill to spin.   [2 marks]

Work Done and Power

I'm sure you're no stranger to <u>doing work</u>, but in physics it's all to do with <u>forces</u> and <u>energy</u>.

If A Force Moves An Object, Work is Done

> When a <u>force</u> moves an object through a <u>distance</u>,
> <u>WORK IS DONE</u> on the object and <u>ENERGY IS TRANSFERRED</u>.

1) To make something <u>move</u>, some sort of <u>force</u> needs to act on it.
   The thing <u>applying the force</u> needs a <u>source</u> of <u>energy</u> (like <u>fuel</u> or <u>food</u>).

2) The force does '<u>work</u>' to <u>move</u> the object and <u>energy</u> is <u>transferred mechanically</u> from one <u>store</u> to another (p.25).

3) Whether energy is transferred '<u>usefully</u>' (e.g. <u>lifting a load</u>) or is '<u>wasted</u>' (p.26) you can still say that '<u>work is done</u>'. Just like Batman and Bruce Wayne, '<u>work done</u>' and '<u>energy transferred</u>' are indeed '<u>one and the same</u>'.

4) You can find out <u>how much</u> work has been done using:

5) <u>One joule of work</u> is done when a <u>force of one newton</u> causes an object to move a <u>distance of one metre</u>. You can also write this as <u>1 J = 1 Nm</u> (newton metre).

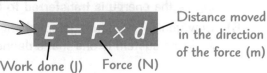

$$E = F \times d$$

Work done (J) Force (N)

Distance moved in the direction of the force (m)

> **EXAMPLE:** Find the energy transferred when a tyre weighing 70 N is lifted 1.2 m into the air.
>
> work done = force × distance = 70 × 1.2 = 84 J

Here, work is being done against gravity. Energy is being transferred to the tyre's gravitational potential energy store.

6) A force doing work often causes a <u>rise in temperature</u> as energy is dissipated to the <u>thermal</u> energy stores of the moving object and its surroundings. This means that the process is <u>wasteful</u> and the <u>efficiency</u> of the process is <u>reduced</u>. Remember, efficiency = useful energy transferred by device (p.26).

   total energy supplied to device

> When you push something along a <u>rough surface</u> (like a <u>carpet</u>) you are doing work <u>against frictional</u> <u>forces</u>. Energy is being <u>transferred</u> to the <u>kinetic energy store</u> of the <u>object</u> because it starts <u>moving</u>, but some is also being transferred to <u>thermal energy stores</u> due to the friction. This causes the overall <u>temperature</u> of the object to <u>increase</u>. (Like <u>rubbing your hands together</u> to warm them up.)

Power is How Much Work is Done per Second

1) <u>Power</u> is the <u>RATE OF ENERGY TRANSFER</u>. The unit of power is the <u>watt</u> (<u>W</u>). <u>1 W = 1 J/s</u>. Another way of describing power is how much <u>work</u> is being done <u>every second</u>.

2) This is the <u>very easy formula</u> for power:

3) The <u>larger</u> the <u>power</u> of an object, the <u>more</u> work it does per second. E.g. if an <u>electric</u> <u>heater</u> has a power of <u>600 W</u> this means it transfers <u>600 J</u> of energy <u>every second</u>. A <u>1200 W</u> heater would transfer <u>twice</u> as much energy per second and so would heat a room <u>quicker</u> than the 600 W heater.

$$\text{power (W)} = \frac{\text{work done (J)}}{\text{time taken (s)}} \quad \text{or} \quad P = \frac{E}{t}$$

> **EXAMPLE:** A motor does 4.8 kJ of work in 2 minutes. Find its power output.
>
> 1) <u>Convert</u> the values to the <u>correct units</u> first (see p.9).   4.8 kJ = 4800 J and 2 mins = 120 s
>
> 2) <u>Substitute</u> the values into the power equation.   P = E ÷ t = 4800 ÷ 120 = 40 W

Watt's power? Power's watts...

Make sure you're happy using the equations on this page before you move on.

Q1   A constant force of 20 N pushes an object 20 cm. Calculate the work done on the object.   [2 marks]

Q2   An appliance transfers 6000 J of energy in 30 seconds. Calculate its power.   [2 marks]

Forces

Force is a <u>vector</u> — it has both a <u>size</u> and a <u>direction</u> (unlike <u>scalar</u> quantities which only have a <u>size</u> — p.12). This means you can use <u>arrows</u> to represent the forces acting on an object or a system.

Interactions Between Objects Cause Forces

1) A <u>force</u> is a <u>push</u> or a <u>pull</u> on an object that is caused by it <u>interacting</u> with something.

2) Sometimes, objects need to be <u>touching</u> for a force to act. E.g. the <u>normal contact force</u> that acts between <u>all</u> touching objects, or <u>friction</u> between a car's <u>tyre</u> and the <u>road</u>. These are <u>contact forces</u>.

3) Other forces can act between objects that <u>aren't touching</u> (<u>non-contact forces</u>). They're usually caused by <u>interacting fields</u>. E.g. the <u>gravitational attraction</u> between objects (like the <u>Earth</u> and the <u>Sun</u>) is caused by their <u>gravitational fields</u> interacting.

4) <u>Interacting magnetic fields</u> (p.85) cause <u>attraction</u> or <u>repulsion</u> between <u>magnetic objects</u>, and the electrostatic force causing <u>attraction</u> and <u>repulsion</u> between <u>electrical charges</u> (p.82) is due to interactions between their <u>electric fields</u> (p.84).

5) Whenever two objects <u>interact</u>, both objects feel an equal but opposite <u>force</u> (Newton's 3rd Law). This pair of forces is called an <u>interaction pair</u>. You can represent an interaction pair with a pair of <u>vectors</u> (<u>arrows</u>).

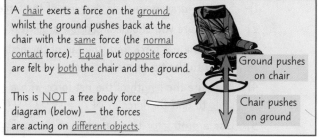

A <u>chair</u> exerts a force on the <u>ground</u>, whilst the ground pushes back at the chair with the <u>same</u> force (the <u>normal contact</u> force). <u>Equal</u> but <u>opposite</u> forces are felt by <u>both</u> the chair and the ground.

This is <u>NOT</u> a free body force diagram (below) — the forces are acting on <u>different objects</u>.

Ground pushes on chair

Chair pushes on ground

Free Body Force Diagrams Show All the Forces Acting on Objects

1) A <u>free body force diagram</u> shows an <u>isolated body</u> (an object or system on its own), and <u>all</u> the <u>forces</u> acting on it.

2) It should include <u>every</u> force acting <u>on the body</u>, but <u>none</u> of the forces it <u>exerts</u> on the rest of the world.

3) The <u>sizes</u> of the arrows show the <u>relative magnitudes</u> of the forces and the <u>directions</u> show the directions of the forces.

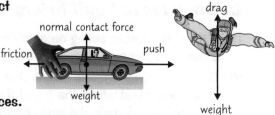

normal contact force
friction
push
weight

drag
weight

A Resultant Force is the Overall Force on a Point or Object

1) In most <u>real</u> situations there are at least <u>two forces</u> acting on an object along any direction.

2) If you have a <u>number of forces</u> acting at a single point, you can replace them with a <u>single force</u> (so long as the single force has the <u>same effect</u> as all the original forces together).

3) This single force is called the <u>resultant force</u> (or sometimes the <u>net force</u> on an object).

4) If the forces all act along the <u>same line</u> (they're all parallel), the <u>overall effect</u> is found by <u>adding</u> those going in the <u>same</u> direction and <u>subtracting</u> any going in the opposite direction.

5) Objects in <u>equilibrium</u> have a resultant force of <u>zero</u> — see the next page. Objects in equilibrium are either <u>stationary</u>, or moving at a <u>steady speed</u> (this is Newton's 1st Law — p.16).

- The <u>normal contact force</u> felt by the van is <u>equal</u> to its weight. These forces act in <u>opposite directions</u>, so there is <u>no resultant force</u> in the <u>vertical</u> direction (1500 N − 1500 N = 0 N).
- The <u>frictional</u> force acting on the van is <u>smaller</u> than the <u>driving</u> force pushing it forward, so there <u>is</u> a <u>resultant force</u> in the <u>horizontal</u> direction.
- 1200 N − 1000 N = 200 N. So the resultant force is <u>200 N (to the left)</u>.

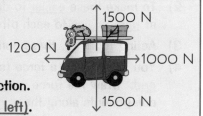

1500 N
1200 N
1000 N
1500 N

Consolidate all your forces into one easy-to-manage force...

Free body force diagrams make most force questions easier, so if you can, always sketch one. Then get to work.

Q1 A car has a driving force of 2000 N and a weight of 1600 N. There is a total resistive force of 1200 N acting against the driving force. Draw the free body force diagram for the car. [2 marks]

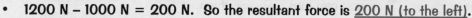

Forces and Vector Diagrams

Scale drawings are useful things — they can help you resolve forces or work out the resultant force.

Use Scale Drawings to Find Resultant Forces

1) Draw all the forces acting on an object, to scale, 'tip-to-tail'.

2) Then draw a straight line from the start of the first force to the end of the last force — this is the resultant (or net) force.

3) Measure the length of the resultant force on the diagram to find the magnitude of the force and the angle to find its direction.

Make sure the scale you use is sensible. You want large, clear diagrams that make your calculations easier to do.

EXAMPLE: A man is on an electric bicycle that has a driving force of 4 N north. However, the wind produces a force of 3 N east. Find the net force acting on the man.

1) Start by drawing a scale drawing of the forces acting.
2) Make sure you choose a sensible scale (e.g. 1 cm = 1 N).
3) Draw the net force from the tail of the first arrow to the tip of the last arrow.
4) Measure the length of the net force with a ruler and use the scale to find the force in N.
5) Use a protractor to measure the direction as a bearing.

A bearing is an angle measured clockwise from north, given as a 3 digit number, e.g. 10° = 010°.

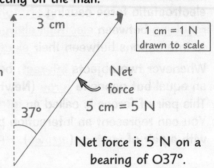

1 cm = 1 N
drawn to scale

Net force
5 cm = 5 N

Net force is 5 N on a bearing of 037°.

An Object is in Equilibrium if the Forces on it are Balanced

1) If all of the forces acting on an object combine to give a resultant force of zero, the object is in equilibrium.

2) On a scale diagram, this means that the tip of the last force you draw should end where the tail of the first force you drew begins. E.g. for three forces, the scale diagram will form a triangle.

3) You might be given forces acting on an object and told to find a MISSING force, given that the object is in equilibrium.

4) To do this, draw out the forces you do know (to scale and tip-to-tail), then join the END of the LAST force to the START of the FIRST force. Make sure you draw this last force in the right direction — it's in the opposite direction to how you'd draw a resultant force.

5) This line is the missing force so you can measure its size and direction.

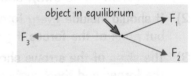
object in equilibrium

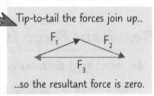
Tip-to-tail the forces join up...
...so the resultant force is zero.

You Can Split a Force into Components

1) Not all forces act horizontally or vertically — some act at awkward angles.

2) To make these easier to deal with, they can be split into two components at right angles to each other (usually horizontal and vertical).

3) Acting together, these components have the same effect as the single force.

4) You can resolve a force (split it into components) by drawing it on a scale grid. Draw the force to scale, and then add the horizontal and vertical components along the gridlines. Then you can just measure them.

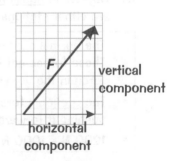
vertical component
horizontal component

Don't blow things out of proportion — it's only scale drawings...

Keep those pencils sharp and those scale drawings accurate — or you'll end up with the wrong answer.

Q1 A remote-controlled boat crosses a stream. The motor provides a 12 N driving force to the west. The river's current causes a force of 5 N north to act on the boat. Find the size of the net force. [2 marks]

Moments

Moments are all about <u>rotations</u>. Read this page thoroughly and don't let yourself get turned around.

A Moment is the Turning Effect of a Force

A <u>force</u>, or several forces, can cause an object to <u>rotate</u>. The <u>turning effect</u> of a force is called its <u>moment</u>. The <u>size</u> of the <u>moment</u> of the force is given by:

> **moment of a force (Nm) = force (N) × distance (m)**

This is actually 'distance normal to the direction of the force'.

1) The <u>force</u> on the spanner causes a <u>turning effect</u> or <u>moment</u> on the nut (which acts as a pivot). A <u>larger force</u> or a <u>longer distance</u> (i.e. a longer spanner) would mean a <u>larger</u> moment.

2) To get the <u>maximum</u> moment (or turning effect) you need to push at <u>right angles</u> (<u>perpendicular</u>) to the spanner. Pushing at <u>any other angle</u> means a <u>smaller distance</u>, and so a <u>smaller moment</u>. This is what the '<u>normal to the direction of the force</u>' bit means.

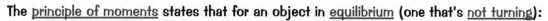

The <u>principle of moments</u> states that for an object in <u>equilibrium</u> (one that's <u>not turning</u>):

> **the sum of the clockwise moments = the sum of the anticlockwise moments**

Levers Make it Easier for us to Do Work

<u>Levers</u> transfer the <u>turning effect</u> of a force — push one end of a lever <u>down</u> and the <u>rotation</u> around the <u>pivot</u> causes the other end to <u>rise</u>.
Levers make it <u>easier to do work</u> as they <u>increase</u> the <u>distance</u> from the pivot at which a <u>force</u> is applied — the longer the lever, the smaller the <u>force</u> needed to give the <u>same moment</u>.

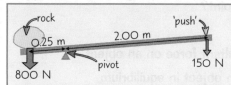

Calculate the moments from <u>each force</u>:

Moment from the rock's weight = F × d = 800 × 0.25 = <u>200 Nm anticlockwise</u>

Moment from the push = F × d = 150 × 2.00 = <u>300 Nm clockwise</u>

So there's a <u>net CLOCKWISE moment of 100 Nm</u>, meaning the <u>rock will rise</u>.

Gears Fit Together to Transmit Turning Effects

1) Gears are <u>circular cogs</u> with '<u>teeth</u>' around their edge. Their teeth <u>interlock</u> so that <u>turning</u> one causes <u>another</u> to turn, in the <u>opposite</u> direction.

2) They are used to <u>transmit</u> the <u>rotational effect</u> of a <u>force</u> from one place to another.

3) A <u>force</u> applied to a <u>small gear</u> creates a <u>small moment</u>. This gear applies the same <u>force</u> to the <u>next gear</u>. If this next gear is <u>larger</u>, this force is applied <u>further</u> from its <u>pivot</u>, so the <u>moment</u> is <u>larger</u>.

4) <u>Interlocked</u> gears will rotate at <u>different speeds</u> — the <u>larger</u> the gear, the <u>slower</u> it spins.

You can work out how the <u>speeds</u> and <u>moments</u> will change between gears by looking at the <u>gear ratios</u>.

For example, look at the three gears above. The largest gear has <u>16 teeth</u> and the medium gear has <u>8 teeth</u>. The <u>ratio of teeth</u> between the largest gear and the medium gear is 16 : 8 = <u>2 : 1</u>. This means that for every <u>1 turn</u> the <u>largest gear</u> does, the <u>medium gear</u> will do <u>2 turns</u>.

The <u>force</u> applied to each gear is the <u>same</u>, and the <u>radius</u> of a gear is equal to the <u>distance</u> of the applied force from the pivot. As <u>moment = force × distance</u>, this means that the <u>ratio of moments</u> of two gears is <u>equal</u> to the <u>ratio of the gears' radii</u>, and therefore equal to the <u>ratio of teeth</u>. For the gears above, the moment of the largest gear to the medium gear is also <u>2 : 1</u> — so the moment gets <u>doubled</u>.

Lubrication (p.27) reduces friction and unwanted energy transfers. Gears are often lubricated to improve the efficiency of machines.

Don't get in a spin — gear up for some more physics...

It's easy to get confused by gear questions. Adding arrows to each gear to show which way it's rotating can help.

Q1   A 10 N force is applied normal to a door, 85 cm from its hinges. Calculate the moment created.   [2 marks]

Revision Questions for Section 4

Well, that's that for <u>Section 4</u> — have a go at these questions, then reward yourself with a nice cup of tea.

- Try these questions and <u>tick off each one</u> when you <u>get it right</u>.
- When you've done <u>all the questions</u> for a topic and are <u>completely happy</u> with it, tick off the topic.

Energy, Work Done and Power (p.65-66) ☑

1) What is a system? ☑
2) Give three ways that the energy of a system can be changed. ☑
3) Give the formula for calculating the work done by a force. ☑
4) Describe how to convert between joules (J) and newton-metres (Nm). ☑
5) True or false? A mechanical process becomes wasteful when it causes an increase in temperature. ☑
6) Define power. State the equation relating power, work done and time. ☑
7) What unit is power measured in? ☑

Forces (p.67-68) ☑

8) True or false? Friction is a non-contact force. ☑
9) What force causes the repulsion of two like electrical charges? What causes this force? ☑
10) What is an interaction pair? ☑
11) What is a free body force diagram? ☑
12) What is meant by the resultant force acting on an object? ☑
13) A parachuter has a weight of 900 N. At one point during his fall, the air resistance acting on him is 500 N. In what direction is his resultant force at this point? ☑
14) What is the resultant force on an object in equilibrium? ☑
15) Describe how you would use a scale diagram to work out the resultant force on an object. ☑
16) True or false? The arrows on a scale diagram for the forces on an object in equilibrium join up to create a closed shape. ☑
17) Describe how you would resolve a force into horizontal and vertical components using a scale drawing. ☑

Moments (p.69) ☑

18) True or false? A moment is a turning effect of a force. ☑
19) State the equation for calculating the size of a moment. ☑
20) What is the principle of moments? ☑
21) Explain how levers make it easier to do work. ☑
22) True or false? For a given force, a larger gear will turn slower than a smaller gear. ☑
23) If a gear is spinning clockwise, what direction will a second gear directly connected to it spin? ☑
24) How can you improve the efficiency of a machine that uses gears? ☑

Current and Circuits

It's pretty bad news if the word <u>current</u> makes you think of delicious cakes instead of physics. Learn what it means, as well as some handy <u>symbols</u> to show items like <u>batteries</u> and <u>switches</u> in a circuit.

Current is the Flow of Electrical Charge

1) <u>Current</u> is the <u>flow</u> of electric charge (e.g. electrons, p.49) around the circuit. Current will <u>only flow</u> through an electrical component if there is a <u>potential difference</u> across that component, and if the circuit is <u>complete</u> (closed). Unit: <u>ampere</u>, **A**.

2) <u>Potential difference</u> (or voltage) is the <u>driving force</u> that <u>pushes</u> the charge round. Unit: <u>volt</u>, **V**.

3) <u>Resistance</u> is anything that <u>slows the flow</u> down. Unit: <u>ohm</u>, Ω.

4) The current flowing <u>through a component</u> depends on the <u>potential difference</u> across it and the <u>resistance</u> of the component (p.72).

Make sure you look back at atomic structure — you need to know it.

potential difference of supply provides the 'push'

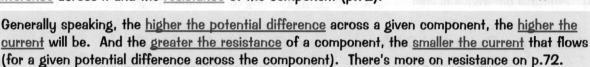

current flows

+ ve   − ve

R

resistance opposes the flow

> Generally speaking, the <u>higher the potential difference</u> across a given component, the <u>higher the current</u> will be. And the <u>greater the resistance</u> of a component, the <u>smaller the current</u> that flows (for a given potential difference across the component). There's more on resistance on p.72.

Total Charge Through a Circuit Depends on Current and Time

1) <u>Current</u> is the <u>rate of flow</u> of <u>charge</u>. In <u>metals</u>, the current is caused by a flow of <u>electrons</u>.

2) If a <u>current</u> (*I*) flows past a point in a circuit for a length of <u>time</u> (*t*), then the <u>charge</u> (*Q*) that has passed this point is given by this formula:

$$\text{charge} = \text{current} \times \text{time}$$

$$\frac{Q}{I \times t}$$

More charge passes around the circuit in a given time when a greater current flows.

3) To use this formula, you need <u>current</u> in <u>amperes</u>, **A**, <u>charge</u> in <u>coulombs</u>, **C**, and <u>time</u> in <u>seconds</u>, **s**.

EXAMPLE:

A battery passes a current of 0.25 A through a light bulb over a period of 4 hours. How much charge does the battery transfer through the bulb altogether?

charge = current × time = 0.25 × (4 × 60 × 60) = **3600 C**

Watch out for units — your time needs to be in seconds if you're calculating charge.

Circuit Symbols You Should Know

There's more about a.c. and d.c. on p.79.

You need to be able to use these symbols to <u>interpret</u> and <u>draw circuit diagrams</u>.

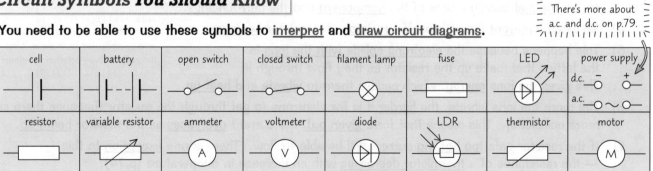

cell	battery	open switch	closed switch	filament lamp	fuse	LED	power supply d.c. − + a.c.
resistor	variable resistor	ammeter	voltmeter	diode	LDR	thermistor	motor

I think it's about time you took charge...

Electrons in circuits actually move from −ve to +ve, but it's conventional to draw current as though it's flowing from +ve to −ve. It's what early physicists thought (before they found out about the electrons), and it's stuck.

Q1   Calculate how long it takes a current of 2.5 A to transfer a charge of 120 C.   [2 marks]

Potential Difference and Resistance

As current flows round a circuit, the charges transfer energy as they struggle against resistance.

Potential Difference is the Energy Transferred Per Unit Charge

1) The potential difference is the energy transferred per coulomb of charge
that passes between two points in an electrical circuit.

2) You can calculate energy transferred, in joules, J, from
charge moved, in C, and potential difference, in V, using this formula:

| energy transferred = charge moved × potential difference | $E = Q \times V$ |

3) So, the potential difference (p.d.) across an electrical component is the amount of energy
transferred by that electrical component (e.g. the amount of energy transferred by a motor
to its kinetic energy store) per unit charge passed. One volt is one joule per coulomb.

4) Potential difference is sometimes called voltage. They're the same thing.

Resistance, Potential Difference and Current: $V = I \times R$

For potential difference (V) in volts, V, current (I) in amps, A, and resistance (R) in ohms, Ω:

| potential difference = current × resistance |

As a formula triangle:

$$\frac{V}{I \times R}$$

If you rearrange this equation, you can use it to calculate the resistance of a component
from measurements of potential difference and current (e.g. from the experiment on the next page).

EXAMPLE:
A 4.0 Ω resistor in a circuit has a potential difference of 6.0 V
across it. What is the current through the resistor?

Rearrange $V = IR$ to give $I = V \div R$, then substitute in the values you have. $I = 6.0 \div 4.0 = 1.5$ A

Since the current of a circuit is affected by its resistance, you can use a variable resistor to
change the current of a supply instead of using a variable supply like the one on the next page.

Resistance Increases with Temperature (Usually)

1) When an electrical charge flows through a component,
it has to do work against resistance.

2) This causes an electrical transfer of energy (work done = energy transferred, p.66).

3) Some of this energy is transferred usefully (p.26) but some of it is dissipated
to the thermal energy stores of the component and the surroundings.

4) So when a current flows through a resistor, the resistor heats up.

5) This happens because the electrons collide with the ions in
the lattice that make up the resistor as they flow through it.
This gives the ions energy, which causes them to vibrate and heat up.

> Low resistance wires (p.91) reduce the
> energy dissipated to thermal stores as
> the current flows between components.

6) The more the ions vibrate, the harder it is for electrons to get through the resistor (because there are
more collisions). This means that for a given p.d. the current decreases as the resistor heats up.

7) If the resistor gets too hot, no current will be able to flow. There is one exception to this
— the resistance of a thermistor decreases with an increase in temperature (p.74).

In the end you'll have to learn this — resistance is futile...

$V = IR$ is one of the most useful equations in electricity — it crops up in a bunch of different places. So make sure
you can bring it to mind super quickly and use it without trouble. Have a quick practise before moving on.

Q1   A current flowing through a resistor transfers 360 J of energy when 75 C of charge
are passed through it. Calculate the potential difference across the resistor.   [2 marks]

Investigating Components

Ooh experiments, you've gotta love 'em. Here's a <u>simple experiment</u> for investigating different components.

The Standard Test Circuit

You can use this circuit to investigate the <u>relationship</u> between <u>current</u> (I), <u>p.d.</u> (V) and <u>resistance</u> for a range of components, such as a <u>filament bulb</u> or a <u>fixed resistor</u>. This relationship can be easily shown with an <u>I-V graph</u> — just like the ones over on the next page.

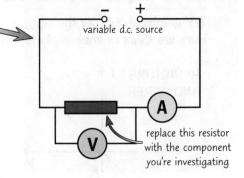

variable d.c. source

replace this resistor with the component you're investigating

The standard test circuit contains:

*   <u>Ammeter</u> — this measures the <u>current</u> (in amps) flowing through the component. It can be put <u>anywhere</u> in the <u>main circuit</u> — but it must be placed <u>in series</u> (p.75) with the component, <u>never</u> in <u>parallel</u>.

*   <u>Voltmeter</u> — this measures the <u>potential difference</u> across the component. It must be placed <u>in parallel</u> (p.75) with the <u>component</u> under test.

PRACTICAL

To use the circuit above to investigate a component, e.g. a <u>fixed resistor</u> or a <u>filament lamp</u>:

1) Connect the circuit as shown above. The <u>component</u> and the <u>ammeter</u> are in <u>series</u>, which means they can be put in <u>any order</u> in the main circuit. (Remember the <u>voltmeter</u> must be <u>in parallel</u> around the <u>component under test</u>.)

2) Change the <u>output potential difference</u> of the <u>power supply</u>. This alters the <u>current</u> flowing through the circuit and the <u>potential difference</u> across the <u>component</u>.

3) Take several <u>pairs of readings</u> from the <u>ammeter</u> and <u>voltmeter</u> to see how the <u>current through</u> the component varies as the <u>potential difference</u> across it is changed.

4) <u>Plot</u> the <u>current</u> against the <u>potential difference</u> to get I-V graphs like the ones on p.74.

5) You can use this data to work out the <u>resistance</u> for <u>each measurement</u> of I and V, using the formula on p.72, so you can see if the resistance of the component <u>changes</u> as I and V change.

6) Make sure the circuit doesn't get <u>too hot</u> over the course of your experiment, as this will mess up your results (p.72). If the circuit starts to warm up, <u>disconnect</u> it for a while between readings so it can cool down. And, like any experiment, you should do repeats and <u>calculate means</u>.

Have a look at page 7 for more about calculating averages and interpreting your results.

You Can Investigate Diodes, LDRs and Thermistors

You can also create <u>I-V graphs</u> for <u>diodes</u>, <u>thermistors</u> and <u>LDRs</u> using the method above (there's more about thermistors and LDRs on the next page). However, the <u>resistance</u> of these components (and so their <u>potential difference</u>) can depend on <u>other factors</u> besides current.

1) <u>Diodes</u> — after you've finished taking measurements for a range of currents, remove the diode and <u>swap its direction</u>. You should find that <u>current cannot flow</u> through the diode anymore (see p.74).

2) <u>Thermistors</u> — keeping the supply potential difference <u>constant</u>, gradually <u>heat</u> the thermistor. (You can do this by placing the thermistor against a beaker of hot water.) You should find that as the <u>temperature increases</u>, the <u>current</u> through the thermistor <u>increases</u> as the <u>resistance decreases</u>.

3) <u>LDRs</u> — conduct your experiment in a <u>dim room</u>. Again keep the p.d. of the supply <u>constant</u> and slowly adjust the light level near to the LDR (e.g. by using a lamp connected to a dimmer switch). You should find as the light level gets <u>brighter</u>, the <u>current</u> through the LDR <u>increases</u> as the <u>resistance decreases</u>.

Measure gymnastics — use a vaultmeter...

Make sure you can describe the experiment above — remember, ammeters in series, voltmeters in parallel.

Q1   Draw a circuit you could use to create an I-V graph for a filament lamp.   [3 marks]

Circuit Devices

With your current and your potential difference measured, you can now make some <u>sweet</u> graphs...

Three Important Current-Potential Difference Graphs

I-V graphs show how the <u>current</u> varies as you <u>change</u> the <u>potential difference</u> (p.d.). Here are three examples, plotted from the experiment on the previous page:

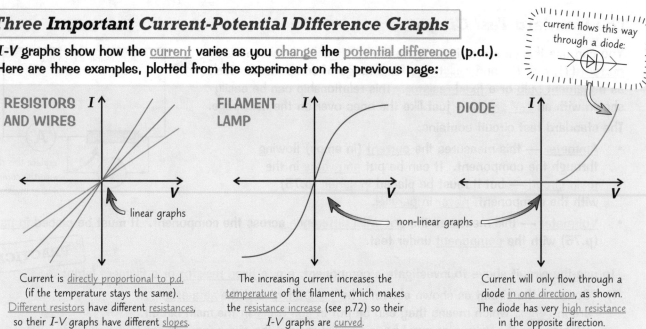

current flows this way through a diode:

RESISTORS AND WIRES

linear graphs

Current is <u>directly proportional to p.d.</u> (if the temperature stays the same). <u>Different resistors</u> have different <u>resistances</u>, so their *I-V* graphs have different <u>slopes</u>.

FILAMENT LAMP

non-linear graphs

The increasing current increases the <u>temperature</u> of the filament, which makes the <u>resistance increase</u> (see p.72) so their *I-V* graphs are <u>curved</u>.

DIODE

Current will only flow through a diode <u>in one direction</u>, as shown. The diode has very <u>high resistance</u> in the opposite direction.

1) <u>Linear</u> components have an *I-V* graph that's a <u>straight line</u> (e.g. a fixed resistor). <u>Non-linear</u> components have a <u>curved</u> *I-V* graph (e.g. a filament lamp or a diode).

2) For <u>linear</u> components, if the line goes through <u>(0,0)</u>, the resistance of the component equals the <u>inverse</u> of the <u>gradient</u> of the line, or "<u>1/gradient</u>". The <u>steeper</u> the graph, the <u>lower</u> the resistance.

3) You can find the <u>resistance</u> for <u>any point</u> on any *I-V* graph by reading the <u>p.d.</u> and <u>current</u> at that point and sticking them into $V = IR$, p.72.

LDR is Short for Light Dependent Resistor

1) An LDR is a resistor that is <u>dependent</u> on the <u>intensity</u> of <u>light</u>. Simple really.

2) In <u>bright light</u>, the resistance <u>falls</u>.

3) In <u>darkness</u>, the resistance is <u>highest</u>.

4) They have lots of applications including <u>automatic night lights</u>, outdoor lighting and <u>burglar detectors</u>.

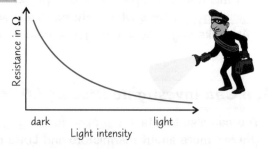

The Resistance of a Thermistor Decreases as Temperature Increases

1) A <u>thermistor</u> is a <u>temperature dependent</u> resistor.

2) In <u>hot</u> conditions, the resistance <u>drops</u>.

3) In <u>cool</u> conditions, the resistance goes <u>up</u>.

4) Thermistors make useful <u>temperature detectors</u>, e.g. <u>car engine</u> temperature sensors and electronic <u>thermostats</u>.

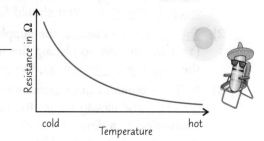

LDRs — Light Dependent Rabbits...

You may get given an *I-V* graph in your exam that you haven't seen before. Make sure you understand why these graphs have the shape they do, and you'll be ready for anything they throw at you.

Q1   Describe one everyday use for: a) an LDR   b) a thermistor   [2 marks]

Series and Parallel Circuits

Make sure you know the <u>rules</u> about what happens to <u>current</u> and <u>p.d.</u> in series and parallel circuits.
You can find out how and why the <u>resistance</u> changes for <u>both</u> of these circuits over on the next page.

Series Circuits — All or Nothing

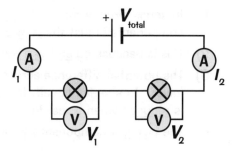

1) In <u>series circuits</u>, the different components are connected <u>in a line</u>, <u>end to end</u>, between the +ve and −ve of the power supply (except for <u>voltmeters</u>, which are always connected <u>in parallel</u>, but they don't count as part of the circuit).

2) If you remove or disconnect <u>one</u> component, the circuit is <u>broken</u> and they all <u>stop working</u>. This is generally <u>not very handy</u>, and in practice <u>very few things</u> are connected in series.

3) You can use the following rules to <u>design</u> series circuits to <u>measure quantities</u> and test components. For a <u>series</u> circuit:

- There's a bigger <u>supply p.d.</u> when more cells are in series (if they're all <u>connected</u> the <u>same way</u>). E.g. when two batteries with a p.d. of 1.5 V are <u>connected in series</u> they supply 3 V <u>between them</u>.
- The <u>current</u> is the <u>same everywhere</u>. $I_1 = I_2 = I_3$ etc. The size of the current depends on the <u>total p.d.</u> and the <u>total resistance</u> of the circuit ($I = V \div R$).
- The total <u>potential difference</u> of the supply is <u>shared</u> between components. The p.d. for each component depends on its <u>resistance</u>.
- The <u>total resistance</u> of the circuit <u>increases</u> as you <u>add</u> resistors (see next page).

Parallel Circuits — Everything is Independent

1) In <u>parallel circuits</u>, each component is <u>separately</u> connected to the +ve and −ve of the <u>supply</u> (except ammeters, which are <u>always</u> connected in <u>series</u>).

2) If you remove or disconnect <u>one</u> of them, it will <u>hardly affect</u> the others at all.

3) This is <u>obviously</u> how <u>most</u> things must be connected, for example in <u>cars</u> and in <u>household electrics</u>. You have to be able to switch everything on and off <u>separately</u>.

This is a branch...
...so is this.

4) Everyday circuits often contain a <u>mixture</u> of series and parallel parts — when looking at components on the <u>same branch</u> the rules for <u>series</u> circuits apply.

5) For a <u>parallel</u> circuit:

- The <u>potential difference</u> is the <u>same</u> across all components. $V_1 = V_2 = V_3$ etc.
- <u>Current</u> is <u>shared</u> between <u>branches</u>. The <u>total current</u> flowing around the circuit is equal to the <u>total</u> of all the currents through the <u>separate components</u>. $I_{total} = I_1 + I_2$ etc.
- In a parallel circuit, there are <u>junctions</u> where the current either <u>splits</u> or <u>rejoins</u>. The total current going <u>into</u> a junction has to equal the total current <u>leaving</u>. (If two <u>identical components</u> are connected in parallel then the <u>same current</u> will flow through each component.)
- The <u>total resistance</u> of the circuit <u>decreases</u> if you add a second resistor in parallel (see p.76).

Series circuits — they're no laughing matter...

Get those rules straightened out in your head, then have a go at these questions to test what you can remember.

Q1 A filament lamp and a resistor are connected in series. A current of 0.5 A flows through the lamp.
State the current flowing through the resistor. [1 mark]

Q2 Draw a circuit diagram for two filament lamps connected in parallel to a battery.
Both of the lamps can be switched on and off without affecting each other. [3 marks]

More on Series and Parallel Circuits

Time for a bit more about <u>series</u> and <u>parallel</u> circuits, including a quick <u>experiment</u>. Fun, fun, fun...

Adding Resistors in Series Increases Total Resistance

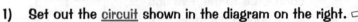

1) In series circuits the <u>total resistance</u> of two components is just the <u>sum</u> of their resistances.

2) This is because by <u>adding a resistor</u> in series, the two resistors have to <u>share</u> the total p.d.

3) The potential difference across each resistor is <u>lower</u>, so the <u>current</u> through each resistor is also lower. In a series circuit, the current is the <u>same everywhere</u> so the total current in the circuit is <u>reduced</u> when a resistor is added. This means the total <u>resistance</u> of the circuit <u>increases</u>.

4) The <u>bigger</u> a component's <u>resistance</u>, the bigger its <u>share</u> of the <u>total potential difference</u>.

Adding a Resistor in Parallel Reduces the Total Resistance

1) If you have <u>two resistors in parallel</u>, their <u>total resistance</u> is <u>less than</u> the resistance of the <u>smallest</u> of the two resistors.

2) This can be tough to get your head around, but think about it like this:

- In <u>parallel</u>, both resistors have the <u>same potential difference</u> across them as the source.
- This means the '<u>pushing force</u>' making the current flow is the <u>same</u> as the <u>source p.d.</u> for each resistor that you add.
- But by adding another loop, the <u>current</u> has <u>more</u> than one direction to go in.
- This increases the <u>total current</u> that can flow around the circuit. Using $V = IR$, an <u>increase in current</u> means a <u>decrease</u> in the <u>total resistance</u> of the circuit.

Use a Circuit to Investigate these Properties

PRACTICAL

1) Set out the <u>circuit</u> shown in the diagram on the right.

2) <u>Vary</u> the <u>output potential difference</u> from the power supply. Record the readings from the <u>ammeter</u> and <u>voltmeter</u> for each change.

3) <u>Replace</u> the <u>resistor</u> with a <u>filament lamp</u> and <u>repeat</u> step 2.

4) Now, connect a <u>second filament lamp</u> to the circuit, <u>in parallel</u> to the first. Connect <u>ammeters</u> and a second <u>voltmeter</u>, so you have:

5) Again, <u>vary</u> the output <u>potential difference</u> of the supply.

6) Write down the <u>current</u> through each ammeter and the <u>p.d.</u> across each <u>component</u>.

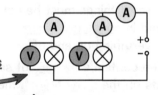

You can also add more resistors to this circuit to see how potential difference is shared across components in series and how the increased resistance affects the current through the circuit.

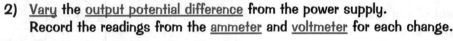

For the <u>series circuit</u>, you should find that as the <u>potential difference increases</u>, the <u>current</u> through the resistor <u>increases</u>. (Using $V = IR$ from page 72 — R for a fixed resistor is <u>constant</u>, so an <u>increase</u> in V causes an <u>increase</u> in I.) You should find a <u>similar</u>, but <u>non-linear</u> relationship between p.d. and current for a filament bulb (see p.74).

For the <u>parallel</u> circuit, you should find that as <u>p.d. increases</u>, so does the <u>current</u> through each bulb (again, this is a <u>non-linear</u> relationship). The <u>p.d.</u> across each bulb is the <u>same</u> as the p.d. of the <u>power supply</u>. You should also notice that the <u>total current</u> through the circuit is the <u>sum</u> of the current through the two <u>branches</u> and that this is <u>larger than</u> the total current through the series circuit with one filament bulb (the <u>overall resistance</u> of the parallel circuit is <u>lower</u>, see above — $V = IR$, so a lower value of R causes a higher value of I).

A current shared *(between identical components)* — is a current halved...

Parallel circuits are more complicated than series circuits but you need to learn about both I'm afraid.

Q1 A 12 V cell is connected in series with a 2 Ω resistor, a 3 Ω resistor and a 7 Ω resistor. Calculate the current through the circuit. [3 marks]

Energy in Circuits

Electrical devices are built to <u>transfer energy</u>. But nothing is perfect and some of this transferred energy ends up in <u>thermal</u> stores. This isn't always a bad thing though — devices like <u>toasters</u> and <u>heaters</u> make use of it.

Energy Transferred *Depends on Current, p.d. and Time*

1) When an electrical <u>charge</u> goes through a <u>change</u> in potential difference, then <u>energy</u> is <u>transferred</u> (as <u>work</u> is done <u>against resistance</u> — p.72).

2) Energy is <u>supplied</u> to the charge at the <u>power source</u> to 'raise' it through a potential.

3) The charge <u>gives up</u> this energy when it '<u>falls</u>' through any <u>potential drop</u> in <u>components</u> elsewhere in the circuit.

4) To find the <u>energy transferred</u> to an electrical component, you can use the equation:

$$E = I \times V \times t$$

Where E is energy transferred in joules (J), I is current in amps (A), V is p.d. in volts (V) and t is time in seconds (s).

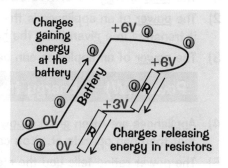
Charges gaining energy at the battery
Charges releasing energy in resistors

This equation comes from combining two of the equations from the next page.

5) The <u>larger</u> the <u>current</u> through, or <u>p.d. across</u>, a component, the more <u>energy</u> is transferred to it.

Energy *is Transferred from Cells and Other Sources*

1) Electrical appliances are designed to <u>transfer energy</u> to components in the circuit when a <u>current</u> flows.

Kettles transfer energy <u>electrically</u> from the mains a.c. supply to the <u>thermal</u> energy store of the heating element inside the kettle.

Energy is transferred <u>electrically</u> from the <u>battery</u> of a handheld fan to the <u>kinetic</u> energy store of the fan's motor.

2) Of course, <u>no</u> appliance transfers <u>all</u> energy completely usefully. The <u>higher</u> the <u>current</u>, the more energy is transferred to the <u>thermal</u> energy stores of the components (and then the surroundings).

3) This <u>heating</u> usually increases the <u>resistance</u> of the components, like you saw on page 72.

Heating a Circuit *isn't Always Bad*

1) Heating up a component generally <u>reduces</u> its <u>efficiency</u> (p.26) — less energy is transferred to <u>useful</u> energy stores because more of it is being transferred to the <u>thermal</u> energy store of the component.

2) If the temperature gets <u>too high</u>, this can cause components in the circuit to <u>melt</u> — which means the circuit will <u>stop working</u>, or not work <u>properly</u>.
More on fuses on p.80.

3) <u>Fuses</u> use this effect to <u>protect</u> circuits — they <u>melt</u> and <u>break</u> the circuit if the current gets too high.

4) The heating effect of an electric current can have other <u>advantages</u>. For example, it's ace if you want to heat something. Toasters contain a coil of wire with a really high <u>resistance</u>. When a current passes through the coil, its temperature increases so much that it <u>glows</u> and gives off <u>infrared radiation</u>. This radiation <u>transfers energy</u> to the bread and <u>cooks</u> it.

5) <u>Filament bulbs</u> and <u>electric heaters</u> work in a similar way.

Have a break from all this work — or you'll have no energy left...

There's no escaping energy transfers I'm afraid. Practise using that equation then take a quick break to recharge.

Q1 A laptop charger is connected to a 230 V source for an hour. A current of 8.0 A flows through it.
Calculate the energy transferred by the laptop charger.
[2 marks]

Power in Circuits

You know that electrical devices <u>transfer energy</u> — well, their <u>power</u> determines how <u>quickly</u> this happens.

Energy Transferred Depends on Power

1) The <u>total</u> energy transferred by an appliance depends on <u>how long</u> the appliance is on for and its <u>power</u>.

2) The <u>power</u> of an appliance is the energy that it <u>transfers per second</u>. So the <u>more</u> energy it transfers in a given time, the <u>higher</u> its power.

3) The <u>power</u> of an appliance can be found using:

> Power (W) = Energy transferred (J) ÷ Time (s)

$$P = \frac{E}{t}$$

4) Appliances are often given a <u>power rating</u> — they're labelled with the <u>maximum</u> safe power that they can operate at. You can usually take this to be their <u>maximum operating power</u>.

5) The power rating tells you the <u>maximum</u> amount of <u>energy</u> transferred between stores <u>per second</u> when the appliance is in use.

> Microwaves have a range of <u>power ratings</u>. A microwave with a power rating of 500 W will take <u>longer</u> to cook food than one with a power rating of 750 W. This is because the 500 W transfers <u>less</u> energy <u>per second</u> to the <u>thermal</u> energy store of the food, so it takes longer to cook.

6) This helps customers choose between models — the <u>lower</u> the power rating, the <u>less</u> electricity an appliance uses in a given time and so the <u>cheaper</u> it is to run.

7) But, a higher power <u>doesn't</u> necessarily mean that it transfers <u>more</u> energy <u>usefully</u>. An appliance may be <u>more powerful</u> than another, <u>but less efficient</u>, meaning that it might still only transfer the <u>same amount</u> of energy (or even <u>less</u>) to useful stores (see p.26).

Power Also Depends on Current and Potential Difference

1) The <u>power transferred</u> by an appliance depends on the <u>potential difference</u> (p.d.) across it, and the <u>current</u> flowing through it.

2) The <u>p.d.</u> tells you how much <u>energy each unit of charge transfers</u> (p.72), and the <u>current</u> tells you <u>how much charge</u> passes per unit time. So <u>both</u> will affect the rate that <u>energy is transferred</u> to an appliance, and the rate at which it <u>transfers energy</u> to other stores.

3) The <u>power</u> of an appliance can be found with:

> Electrical power (W) = Current (A) × Potential difference (V)

$$P = IV$$

4) You can use this equation to work out the fuse (p.80) that should be used in an appliance. To work out the size of the <u>fuse</u> needed, you need to work out the <u>current</u> that the item will normally use:

> **EXAMPLE:** A 1 kW hair dryer is connected to a 230 V supply. Find the fuse needed.
> 1) Use the equation to find the normal current.
> 2) A fuse is usually rated just a little higher than the normal current.
>
> $I = P \div V = 1000 \div 230 = 4.3 \text{ A}$
> So a 5 amp fuse is needed.

5) You can also find the power if you <u>don't know</u> the <u>potential difference</u>. To do this, stick $V = IR$ from page 72 into $P = IV$, which gives you:

$$P = I^2R$$

Where P is the electrical power in watts (W), I is current in amperes (A) and R is the resistance in ohms (Ω).

You have the power — now use your potential...

I'm afraid the best way to learn all of this is to just practise using those equations again and again. Sorry.

Q1 Calculate the difference in the amount of energy transferred by a 250 W TV and a 375 W TV when they are both used for two hours. [3 marks]

Electricity in the Home

There are two types of electricity supply — <u>alternating</u> and <u>direct currents</u>. Read on for more about both...

Mains Supply is a.c., Battery Supply is d.c.

1) There are two types of electricity supplies — <u>alternating current</u> (a.c.) and <u>direct current</u> (d.c.).

2) In <u>a.c. supplies</u> the movement of the charges is <u>constantly</u> changing direction. <u>Alternating currents</u> are produced by <u>alternating voltages</u> (the <u>positive</u> and <u>negative</u> ends of the p.d. keep <u>alternating</u>).

3) The <u>UK mains supply</u> (the electricity in your home) is an a.c. supply at around <u>230 V</u>.

4) The frequency of the a.c. mains supply is <u>50 cycles per second</u> or <u>50 Hz</u> (hertz).

5) By contrast, cells and batteries supply <u>direct current</u> (d.c.).

6) In <u>direct current</u> the movement of the charges is only in one <u>direction</u>. It's created by a <u>direct voltage</u> (a p.d. that is <u>only positive</u> or <u>negative</u>, not both).

> You can turn a.c. into d.c. by using a diode (p.74).

Most Cables Have Three Separate Wires

1) Most electrical appliances are connected to the mains supply by <u>three-core</u> cables. This means that they have <u>three wires</u> inside them, each with a <u>core of copper</u> and a <u>coloured plastic coating</u>.

2) The <u>colour</u> of the insulation on each cable shows its <u>purpose</u>.

3) The colours are <u>always</u> the <u>same</u> for <u>every</u> appliance. This is so that it's easy to tell the different wires <u>apart</u>.

2) <u>NEUTRAL WIRE</u> — <u>blue</u>.
The neutral wire <u>completes</u> the circuit — when the appliance is operating normally, current flows through the <u>live</u> and <u>neutral</u> wires. It is around <u>0 V</u>.

1) <u>LIVE WIRE</u> — <u>brown</u>.
The live wire carries the voltage (potential difference, p.d.). It alternates between a <u>high +ve and –ve voltage</u> of about <u>230 V</u>.

3) <u>EARTH WIRE</u> — <u>green</u> and <u>yellow</u>.
The earth wire is for <u>safety</u> and <u>protecting</u> the <u>wiring</u>. It carries the current away if something goes <u>wrong</u> and stops the appliance casing becoming <u>live</u>. It's <u>also</u> at 0 V.

- The <u>p.d.</u> between the <u>live wire</u> and the <u>neutral wire</u> equals the <u>supply p.d.</u> (<u>230 V</u> for the mains).
- The <u>p.d.</u> between the <u>live wire</u> and the <u>earth wire</u> is also <u>230 V</u> for a mains-connected appliance.
- There is <u>no p.d.</u> between the <u>neutral wire</u> and the <u>earth wire</u> — they're both at 0 V.

4) <u>Plug sockets</u> have <u>switches</u> which are connected in the <u>live wire</u> of the circuit. This is so the circuit can be <u>broken</u> — the appliance becomes <u>isolated</u> and the risk of an <u>electric shock</u> is reduced.

Touching the Live Wire Gives You an Electric Shock

1) Your <u>body</u> (just like the earth) is at <u>0 V</u>.

2) This means that if you touch the <u>live wire</u>, a <u>large potential difference</u> is produced across your body and a <u>current</u> flows through you.

3) This causes a large <u>electric shock</u> which could injure or even kill you.

4) Even if a plug socket or a light switch is turned <u>off</u> (i.e. the switch is <u>open</u>) there is still a <u>danger</u> of an electric shock. A current <u>isn't flowing</u>, but there is still a p.d. in the live wire. If you made <u>contact</u> with the live wire, your body would provide a <u>link</u> between the supply and the earth, so a <u>current</u> would flow <u>through you</u>.

5) <u>Any</u> connection between <u>live</u> and <u>neutral</u> can be <u>dangerous</u>. If the link creates a <u>low resistance</u> path to earth, a huge current will flow, which could result in a fire.

Why are earth wires green and yellow — when mud is brown..?

Electricity is very useful, but it can also be very dangerous. Make sure you know the risks.

Q1 Explain the difference between a.c. and d.c. electricity supplies. [2 marks]

Fuses and Earthing

Fuses and circuit breakers are super important. And questions on them cover a whole barrel of fun —
electrical current, resistance, potential difference... Read this page and make sure you've got it sussed.

Earthing and Fuses Prevent Electrical Overloads

Surges (sudden increases) in current can occur because of changes in a circuit (e.g. an appliance suddenly switching off) or because of a fault in an electrical appliance. Current surges can lead to the circuits and wiring in your appliances melting or causing a fire, and faulty appliances can cause deadly electric shocks.

The earth wire and a fuse are included in electrical appliances
to prevent this from happening. This is how they work:

1) If a fault develops in which the live wire somehow touches the metal case, then because the case is earthed, too great a current flows through the live wire, the case and the earth wire.

2) This surge in current melts the fuse when the amount of current is greater than the fuse rating. Fuses are connected to the live wire, so that breaking the fuse breaks the circuit and cuts off the live supply.

3) This isolates the whole appliance, making it impossible to get an electric shock from the case. It also prevents the risk of fire caused by the heating effect of a large current.

4) Fuses should be rated as near as possible but just higher than the normal operating current.

5) The larger the current, the thicker the cable you need to carry it (to stop the cable getting too hot and melting). That's why the fuse rating needed for cables usually increases with cable thickness.

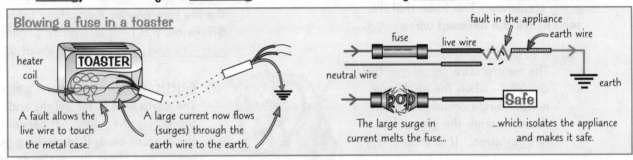

Blowing a fuse in a toaster

heater coil — TOASTER — A fault allows the live wire to touch the metal case. — A large current now flows (surges) through the earth wire to the earth.

fuse — live wire — fault in the appliance — earth wire — neutral wire — earth — The large surge in current melts the fuse... — Safe — ...which isolates the appliance and makes it safe.

6) As well as the fuses in plugs, there are also household fuses (these are the ones that blow when a light bulb goes). These work in the same way, but protect the wiring in the house, not just in an appliance.

Circuit Breakers are Even Safer Than Fuses

Circuit breakers can be used in the place of household fuses.

1) Instead of melting a fuse, a large current may instead 'trip' (turn off) a circuit breaker.
2) Circuit breakers turn off quicker than the time taken for a fuse to melt.
3) They can also be reset, which is much easier than having to replace a fuse.
4) However, circuit breakers are more expensive than fuses.

Insulating Materials Make Appliances "Double Insulated"

1) All appliances with metal cases are usually "earthed" to reduce the danger of electric shock.
2) "Earthing" just means the case must be attached to an earth wire.
An earthed conductor can never become live.
3) If the appliance has a plastic casing and no metal parts showing then it's said to be double insulated.
4) Anything with double insulation like that doesn't need an earth wire — just a live and neutral.
Cables that only carry the live and neutral wires are known as two-core cables.

Nothing shocks my mum — she's very down to earth...

Earthing is dead important, so make sure you understand it and the life-saving protection it provides.

Q1   Which wire are fuses connected in?   [1 mark]

Revision Questions for Section 5

Well, that wraps up <u>Section 5</u> — time to have a go at a few questions to see how much you can remember.

- Try these questions and <u>tick off each one</u> when you <u>get it right</u>.
- When you've done <u>all the questions</u> for a subtopic and are <u>completely happy</u> with it, tick off the topic.

Circuit Basics (p.71-74) ☑

1) What is meant by potential difference and resistance in a circuit? ☑
2) Define current and state an equation that links current, charge and time, with units for each. ☑
3) Draw the circuit symbols for: a cell, a filament lamp, a diode, a motor and an LDR. ☑
4) Give the equation that links energy transferred, charge moved and potential difference. ☑
5) What is the equation that links potential difference, current and resistance? ☑
6) Briefly explain why resistance increases with temperature for a resistor. ☑
7) Explain how you would investigate how the current through a component affected its resistance. ☑
8) True or false? An ammeter must be connected in parallel to the component being tested. ☑
9) Name one linear component and one non-linear component. ☑
10) Explain how the resistance of an LDR varies with light intensity. ☑
11) Give one everyday use of an LDR. ☑
12) What happens to the resistance of a thermistor as it gets hotter? ☑

Series and Parallel Circuits (p.75-76) ☑

13) How does the current through each component vary in a series circuit? ☑
14) True or false? Potential difference is shared between components in a series circuit. ☑
15) How does potential difference vary between components connected in parallel? ☑
16) True or false? Adding resistors in series increases the total resistance of the circuit. ☑
17) Does adding two resistors in parallel increase or decrease the total resistance of a circuit? ☑

Power and Energy Transfers in Circuits (p.77-78) ☑

18) Write down the equation that links energy transferred, current, potential difference and time. ☑
19) Give two disadvantages of the heating effect in an electrical circuit. ☑
20) Give two advantages of the heating effect in an electrical circuit. ☑
21) Define power in terms of energy transferred. ☑
22) What is a power rating? ☑
23) State the equation that links electrical power, current and potential difference. ☑
24) What is the third equation for electrical power, which links current and resistance? ☑

Electricity in the Home and Electrical Safety (p.79-80) ☑

25) True or false? Mains supply electricity is an alternating current. ☑
26) What is the frequency of the UK mains supply? ☑
27) Why are the three wires in a three-core cable colour coded? ☑
28) Give the potential differences for the three wires in a three-core mains cable. ☑
29) Explain why touching a live wire is dangerous. ☑
30) Explain how a fuse protects you if a fault causes the live wire to touch the metal case of an appliance. ☑
31) True or false? Circuit breakers must be replaced each time they 'trip'. ☑

Static Electricity

Static electricity builds up on insulating materials and often ends with a spark or a shock.

Build-up of Static is Caused by Friction

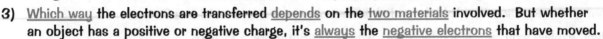

1) When certain insulating materials are rubbed together, negatively charged electrons will be scraped off one and dumped on the other.

2) As the materials are insulators, these electrons are not free to move — this build up of charge is static electricity. The materials become electrically charged, with a positive static charge on the one that has lost electrons and an equal negative static charge on the other.

3) Which way the electrons are transferred depends on the two materials involved. But whether an object has a positive or negative charge, it's always the negative electrons that have moved.

4) The classic examples are polythene and acetate rods being rubbed with a cloth duster (shown above).

Like Charges Repel, Opposite Charges Attract

1) Electrically charged objects exert a force on one another.

2) Two things with opposite electric charges are attracted to each other, while two things with the same electric charge will repel each other.

3) These forces get weaker the further apart the two things are.

4) One way to see these forces is to suspend a rod with a known charge from a piece of string (so it is free to move). Placing an object with the same charge nearby will repel the rod — the rod will move away from the object. An oppositely-charged object will attract the rod, causing it to move towards the object.

Electrically Charged Objects can Attract Uncharged Objects

1) Rubbing a balloon against your hair or clothes transfers electrons to the balloon, leaving it with a negative charge. If you then hold the balloon against a wall it will stick, even though the wall isn't charged.

2) That's because the charges on the surface of the wall can move a little — the negative charges on the balloon repel the negative charges on the surface of the wall.

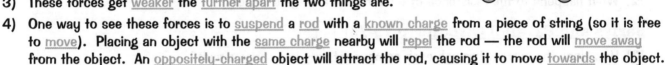

3) This leaves a positive charge on the surface, which attracts the negatively charged balloon. This is called attraction by induction. And there are plenty more examples of it, too...

4) If you run a comb through your hair, electrons will be transferred to the comb making it negatively charged. It can then be used to pick up little pieces of uncharged paper — holding it near the little pieces of paper causes induction in the paper, which means they jump up and stick to the comb.

Too Much Static Causes Sparks

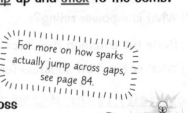

For more on how sparks actually jump across gaps, see page 84.

1) As electric charge builds on an object, the potential difference between the object and the earth (which is at 0 V) increases.

2) If the potential difference gets large enough, electrons can jump across the gap between the charged object and the earth — this is the spark.

3) They can also jump to any earthed conductor that is nearby — which is why you can get static shocks from clothes, or getting out of a car.

4) This usually happens when the gap is fairly small. (But not always — lightning is just a really big spark.)

Stay away from electrons — they're a negative influence...

Electrons jumping about the place and giving us all shocks, the cheeky so-and-sos.

Q1   Jade removes her jumper in a dark room. As she does so, she hears a crackling noise and sees tiny sparks of light between her jumper and her shirt. Explain the cause of this.   [3 marks]

Uses and Dangers of Static Electricity

Static electricity can be a bit of a nuisance sometimes, but it also has some good uses, e.g. in industry. But don't get too happy clappy about how wonderful static electricity is — it can be pretty dangerous too.

Static Electricity Is Used in Electrostatic Sprayers

1) Photocopiers use static electricity to copy images onto a charged plate before printing them.
2) Static electricity can be used to reduce the dust and smoke that rises out of industrial chimneys.
3) Another use of static electricity is electrostatic sprayers:

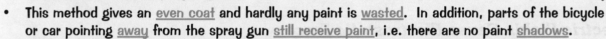

- Electrostatic sprayers are used in various industries to give a fine, even coat of whatever's being sprayed. The classic examples are insecticide sprayers and paint sprayers.
- Bikes and cars are painted using electrostatic paint sprayers.
- The spray gun is charged, which charges up the small drops of paint. Each paint drop repels all the others, since they've all got the same charge, so you get a very fine, even spray.
- The object to be painted is given an opposite charge to the gun. This attracts the fine spray of paint.
- This method gives an even coat and hardly any paint is wasted. In addition, parts of the bicycle or car pointing away from the spray gun still receive paint, i.e. there are no paint shadows.
- Insecticide sprayers work in a similar way, except the crops to be sprayed aren't given an opposite charge — the plants charge by induction as the insecticide droplets come near them (see p.82).

Static Electricity Can be Dangerous

Whilst there are some uses of static electricity, it can be inconvenient and sometimes even dangerous.

1) Refueling cars — as fuel flows out of a filler pipe, e.g. into an aircraft or tanker, then static can build up. This can easily lead to a spark (p.82) which might cause an explosion in dusty or fumey places — like when filling up a car with fuel at a petrol station.
2) Static on airplanes — as planes fly through the air, friction between the air and the plane causes the plane to become charged. This build up of static charge can interfere with communication equipment.
3) Lightning — raindrops and ice bump together inside storm clouds, leaving the top of the cloud positively charged and the bottom of the cloud negative. This creates a huge voltage and a big spark, which can damage homes or start fires when it strikes the ground.
4) You can reduce some of these dangers by earthing charged objects (see below).

Objects Can be Earthed to Stop Electrostatic Charge Building Up

1) Dangerous sparks can be prevented by connecting a charged object to the ground using a conductor (e.g. a copper wire) — this is called earthing.
2) Earthing provides an easy route for the static charges to travel into the ground. This means no charge can build up to give you a shock or make a spark.
3) The electrons flow down the conductor to the ground if the charge is negative and flow up the conductor from the ground if the charge is positive.
4) Fuel tankers must be earthed to prevent any sparks that might cause the fuel to explode.

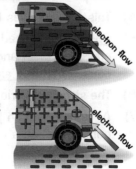

I know, I know — yet another shocking joke...

As useful as static electricity can be, you've got to be aware of the dangers — and how to prevent them.

Q1   Give two uses of static electricity.   [2 marks]

Electric Fields

Electric fields — much less green and much more shocking than the fields you're used to.

Electric Charges Create an Electric Field

1) An electric field is created around any electrically charged object.
   It's the region around a charged object where, if a second charged object was
   placed inside it, a force would be exerted on both of the charges (see below).

2) The closer to the object you get, the stronger the field is. (And the further from it, the weaker it is.)

3) You can show an electric field around an object using field lines. For example, you can
   draw the field lines for an isolated (i.e. not interacting with anything) point charge:

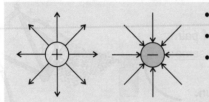

Draw at least eight equally spaced field lines.

- Electric field lines go from positive to negative.
- They're always at a right angle to the surface.
- The closer together the lines are, the stronger the field is
  — you can see that the further from a charge you go, the
  further apart the lines are and so the weaker the field is.

Electric Fields Cause Electrostatic Forces

1) When a charged object is placed in an electric field, it feels a force.
   This force is caused by the electric fields around two charged objects interacting.

2) If the field lines between the charged objects point in the same direction,
   the field lines 'join up' and the objects are attracted to each other.

3) When the field lines between the charged objects point in opposite directions,
   the field lines 'push against' each other and the objects repel each other.

4) Between two oppositely-charged parallel plates,
   you get a uniform field that looks like this.

5) The strength and direction of the field is
   the same anywhere between the two plates
   (it's only different at the very ends).

If you need to draw electric fields, don't forget the arrows on your field lines.

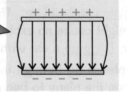

When you're drawing a uniform field, you need to show at least three field lines, parallel and all the same distance apart.

Sparking Can Be Explained By Electric Fields

1) When an object becomes statically charged, it generates its own electric field.

2) Interactions between this field and other objects are the cause of events like sparking.

3) For example, for the comb from p.82 — after it's been run through your hair,
   it's charged and so produces an electric field. This electric field interacts with
   the pieces of paper (without touching them) and so they feel a force.

4) This force causes them to move towards the comb (and some will even stick to it).

5) Sparks are caused when there is a high enough potential difference between a
   charged object and the earth (or an earthed object). A high potential difference
   causes a strong electric field between the charged object and the earthed object.

6) The strong electric field causes electrons in the air particles to be removed (known as ionisation).

7) Air is normally an insulator, but when it is ionised it is much more
   conductive, so a current can flow through it. This is the spark.

Electric felines — lines between charged cats...

Electric fields may seem a bit weird at first — but the good news is they're very similar to magnetic fields
(which are over on the next page), so if you understand one of them, you can understand them both.

Q1   Draw the field lines surrounding an isolated, uniform, positively-charged sphere.   [3 marks]

Magnets and Magnetic Fields

I think magnetism is an <u>attractive</u> subject, but don't get <u>repelled</u> by the exam — <u>revise</u>.

Magnets Produce Magnetic Fields

To see the shape of a magnetic field, place a piece of card over a magnet and sprinkle iron filings onto it. The filings line up with the field lines — but they won't show you the direction of the field.

1) All magnets have <u>two poles</u> — <u>north</u> and <u>south</u>.

2) All magnets produce a <u>magnetic field</u> — a region where <u>other magnets</u> or <u>magnetic materials</u> (see next page) experience a <u>force</u>.

3) You can show a magnetic field by drawing <u>magnetic field lines</u>.

4) The lines always go from <u>north to south</u> and they show <u>which way</u> a force would act on a north pole at that point in the field.

5) The <u>closer together</u> the lines are, the <u>stronger</u> the magnetic field.

6) The <u>further away</u> from a magnet you get, the <u>weaker</u> the field is.

7) The magnetic field is <u>strongest</u> at the <u>poles</u> of a magnet. This means that the <u>magnetic forces</u> are also <u>strongest</u> at the poles.

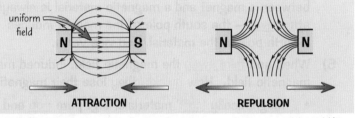

a north pole here would feel a force to the right

Magnetic Fields Cause Forces between Magnets

1) Between <u>two magnets</u> the magnetic force can be <u>attractive</u> or <u>repulsive</u>. Two poles that are the same (these are called <u>like poles</u>) will <u>repel</u> each other. Two <u>unlike</u> poles will <u>attract</u> each other.

2) Placing the north and south poles of two bar magnets <u>near</u> each other creates a <u>uniform field</u> between the two poles. The magnetic field is the <u>same strength</u> everywhere between the poles.

3) If you're asked to <u>draw</u> a uniform magnetic field, you need to draw <u>at least three</u> field lines, <u>parallel</u> to each other and all the <u>same distance</u> apart.

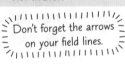

uniform field

ATTRACTION   **REPULSION**

Don't forget the arrows on your field lines.

Plotting Compasses Show the Directions of Magnetic Fields

1) Inside a compass is a tiny <u>bar magnet</u> called a <u>needle</u>. A compass needle always <u>lines up</u> with the magnetic field it's in.

2) You can use a compass to build up a picture of what the field around a magnet <u>looks like</u>:

    The compass follows the field lines and points towards the south pole of the bar magnet.

    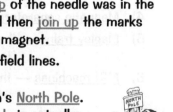

    • Put the magnet on a <u>piece of paper</u> and <u>draw round it</u>.

    • Place the compass on the paper <u>near</u> the magnet. The needle will point in the <u>direction</u> of the <u>field line</u> at this position.

    • Mark the direction of the <u>compass needle</u> by drawing two dots — one at each end of the needle.

    • Then <u>move</u> the compass so that the <u>tail end</u> of the needle is where the <u>tip</u> of the needle was in the <u>previous position</u> and put a dot by the tip of the needle. Repeat this and then <u>join up</u> the marks you've made — you'll end up with a <u>drawing</u> of one <u>field line</u> around the magnet.

    • Repeat this method at different points around the magnet to get several field lines. Make sure you draw <u>arrows</u> from north to south on your field lines.

3) When they're not near a magnet, compasses always point towards the Earth's <u>North Pole</u>. This is because the <u>Earth</u> generates its own <u>magnetic field</u> (and the <u>North Pole</u> is actually a <u>magnetic south pole</u>). This shows the <u>inside</u> (<u>core</u>) of the Earth must be <u>magnetic</u>.

Magnets are like farmers — surrounded by fields...

Magnetism is one of those things that takes a while to make much sense. Learn these basics — you'll need them.

Q1   Draw the magnetic field lines for a bar magnet. Label the areas where the field is strongest.   [3 marks]

Q2   Describe how to plot the magnetic field lines of a bar magnet using a compass.   [4 marks]

Permanent and Induced Magnets

Magnetic fields don't just affect <u>magnets</u> — they affect a few special <u>magnetic materials</u> too.

Very Few Materials are Magnetic

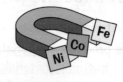

1) The main <u>three</u> magnetic elements are <u>iron</u>, <u>nickel</u> and <u>cobalt</u>.
2) Some alloys and compounds of these metals are also magnetic.
   For example, <u>steel</u> is magnetic because it contains <u>iron</u>.
3) If you put a magnetic material near a magnet, it is <u>attracted</u> to that magnet.
   The magnetic force between a magnet and a magnetic material is <u>always</u> attractive.

Magnets Can be Permanent or Induced

1) <u>Permanent</u> magnets (e.g. bar magnets) produce
   their own magnetic field <u>all the time</u>.
2) <u>Induced</u> (or <u>temporary</u>) magnets only produce a
   magnetic field while they're <u>in</u> another <u>magnetic field</u>.
3) If you put any <u>magnetic material</u> into a magnetic
   field, it becomes an <u>induced</u> magnet.
4) This <u>magnetic induction</u> explains why the force
   between a magnet and a magnetic material is always
   <u>attractive</u> — the south pole of the magnet induces
   a north pole in the material, and vice versa.

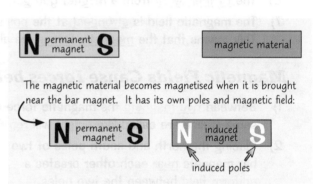

The magnetic material becomes magnetised when it is brought near the bar magnet. It has its own poles and magnetic field:

induced poles

5) When you <u>take away</u> the magnetic field, induced magnets return to normal and <u>stop producing</u> a
   magnetic field. How <u>quickly</u> they lose their magnetism depends on the material they're made from.
   - Magnetically '<u>soft</u>' materials, e.g. pure <u>iron</u> and <u>nickel-iron alloys</u>, lose their magnetism very quickly.
   - Magnetically '<u>hard</u>' materials, e.g. <u>steel</u>, lose their magnetism more slowly.
     <u>Permanent magnets</u> are made from magnetically hard materials.

Magnetic Materials have Lots of Uses

There are many different <u>uses</u> of <u>magnetic materials</u>, the number of which has grown since the invention
of <u>electromagnets</u> (p.88). For example:

1) <u>Fridge doors</u> — there is a <u>permanent</u> magnetic strip in your fridge door to keep it closed.
2) <u>Cranes</u> — these use <u>induced</u> electromagnets to <u>attract</u> and <u>move</u> magnetic
   materials — e.g. moving <u>scrap metal</u> in scrap yards.
3) <u>Doorbells</u> — these use <u>electromagnets</u> which turn <u>on</u> and <u>off</u> rapidly, to repeatedly attract
   and release an arm which <u>strikes</u> the metal bell to produce a <u>ringing</u> noise.
4) <u>Magnetic separators</u> — these are used in recycling plants to <u>sort metal items</u> (like cans).
5) <u>Maglev trains</u> — these use <u>magnetic repulsion</u> to make trains <u>float</u> slightly above the track
   (to reduce losses from <u>friction</u>) and to <u>propel</u> them along.
6) <u>MRI machines</u> — these use magnetic fields to create <u>images</u> of the inside of your body
   without having to use <u>ionising radiation</u> (like X-rays, p.47).
7) <u>Speakers and microphones</u> — there's more about these on page 90.

Attractive pend with a magnetic personality — I'm a catch...

Remember, induced magnets are also called temporary because they're only magnetic when in a magnetic field.

Q1   State three everyday uses of magnetic materials.   [3 marks]

Q2   Give two differences between permanent and induced magnets.   [2 marks]

Electromagnetism and the Motor Effect

On this page you'll see that a magnetic field is also found around a wire that has a current passing through it.

A Moving Charge Creates a Magnetic Field

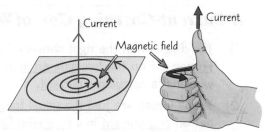

The Right-Hand Thumb Rule
Using your right hand, point your thumb in the direction of current and curl your fingers. The direction of your fingers is the direction of the field.

1) When a current flows through a long, straight conductor (e.g. a wire) a magnetic field is created around it.

2) The field is made up of concentric circles perpendicular to the wire, with the wire in the centre.

3) Changing the direction of the current changes the direction of the magnetic field — use the right-hand thumb rule to work out which way it goes. (In experiments, you can use a plotting compass to find its direction, p.85.)

4) The larger the current through the wire, or the closer to the wire you are, the stronger the field is.

The Motor Effect — A Current in a Magnetic Field Experiences a Force

When a current-carrying conductor (e.g. a wire) is put between magnetic poles, the two magnetic fields interact. The result is a force on the wire.

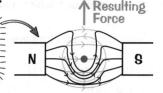

This is an aerial view. The red dot represents a wire carrying current "out of the page" (towards you). (If it was a cross ('×') then that would mean the current was going into the page.)

→ Normal magnetic field of wire
⇢ Normal magnetic field of magnets
→ **Deviated magnetic field of magnets**

The wire also exerts an equal and opposite force on the magnet (from Newton's Third Law, see p.19) but we're just looking at the force on the wire.

1) To experience the full force, the wire has to be at 90° (right angles) to the magnetic field. If the wire runs along the magnetic field, it won't experience any force at all. At angles in between, it'll feel some force.

2) The force always acts in the same direction relative to the magnetic field and the direction of the current in the wire. So changing the direction of either the magnetic field or the current will change the direction of the force.

→ Current
→ Magnetic field
→ Force

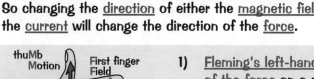

1) Fleming's left-hand rule is used to find the direction of the force on a current-carrying conductor.

2) Using your left hand, point your First finger in the direction of the magnetic Field and your seCond finger in the direction of the Current.

3) Your thuMb will then point in the direction of the force (Motion).

You Can Find the Size of the Force Using F = BIl

The force acting on a conductor in a magnetic field depends on three things:

1) The magnetic flux density — how many field (flux) lines there are in a region. This shows the strength of the magnetic field (p.85).

2) The size of the current through the conductor.

3) The length of the conductor that's in the magnetic field.

When the current is at 90° to the magnetic field it is in, the force acting on it can be found using the equation on the right.

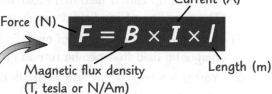

Force (N)
$$F = B \times I \times l$$
Current (A)
Magnetic flux density (T, tesla or N/Am)
Length (m)

Left-hand rule for the motor effect — drive on the left...

Learn the left-hand rule and use it — don't be scared of looking like a muppet in the exam.

Q1 A 35 cm long piece of wire is at 90° to an external magnetic field. The wire experiences a force of 0.98 N when a current of 5.0 A is flowing through it. Calculate the magnetic flux density of the field. [2 marks]

Motors and Solenoids

Electric motors might look a bit tricky, but it's really just applying the stuff you learnt on the previous page.

A Current-Carrying Coil of Wire Rotates in a Magnetic Field

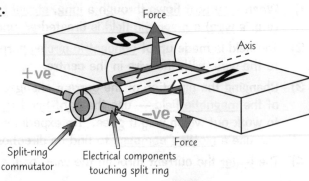

1) The diagram on the right shows a basic d.c. motor. Forces act on the two side arms of a coil of wire that's carrying a current.

2) These forces are just the usual forces which act on any current in a magnetic field (p.87).

3) These forces act in opposite directions on each side, so the coil rotates.

4) The split-ring commutator is a clever way of swapping the contacts every half turn to keep the motor rotating in the same direction.

5) The direction of the motor can be reversed either by swapping the polarity of the d.c. supply (reversing the current) or swapping the magnetic poles over (reversing the field).

6) You can use Fleming's left-hand rule to work out which way the coil will turn.

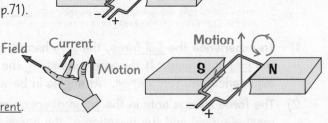

EXAMPLE: Is the coil turning clockwise or anticlockwise?

1) Draw in current arrows (from positive to negative, p.71).

2) Use Fleming's left-hand rule on one branch (here, I've picked the right-hand branch).

3) Point your first finger in the direction of the magnetic field (remember, this is north to south).

4) Point your second finger in the direction of the current.

5) Draw in the direction of motion (the direction your thumb is pointing in).

The coil is turning anticlockwise.

A Solenoid is a Long Coil of Wire

1) Around a single loop of current-carrying wire, the magnetic field looks like this:

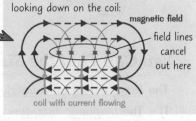

2) You can increase the strength of the magnetic field produced by a length of wire by wrapping it into a long coil with lots of loops, called a solenoid.

3) The field lines around each separate loop of wire line up.

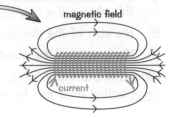

- Inside the solenoid, you get lots of field lines pointing in the same direction. The magnetic field is strong and almost uniform.

- Outside the coil, the overlapping field lines cancel each other out — so the field is weak apart from at the ends of the solenoid.

4) You end up with a field that looks like the one around a bar magnet. The direction of the field depends on the direction of the current (p.87).

5) A solenoid is an example of an ELECTROMAGNET — a magnet with a magnetic field that can be turned on and off using an electric current.

6) You can increase the field strength of the solenoid even more by putting a block of iron in the centre of the coil. This iron core becomes an induced magnet (see p.86) whenever current is flowing.

Give me one good raisin why I should make the currant joke...

Motors and solenoids are used in loads of everyday things from speakers to alarm clocks.

Q1   Sketch the magnetic field in and around a solenoid.   [3 marks]

Electromagnetic Induction in Transformers

Transformers use electromagnetic induction — don't panic, it's not as bad as it sounds.

A Changing Magnetic Field Induces a Potential Difference in a Conductor

Electromagnetic Induction: The induction of a potential difference (and current if there's a complete circuit) in a wire which is experiencing a change in magnetic field.

Induces is a fancy word for creates.

1) There are two different situations where you get electromagnetic induction. The first is if an electrical conductor (e.g. a coil of wire) and a magnetic field move relative to each other.
   - You can do this by moving/rotating either a magnet in a coil of wire OR a conductor (wire) in a magnetic field ("cutting" magnetic field lines).
   - If you move or rotate the magnet (or conductor) in the opposite direction, then the p.d./current will be reversed. Likewise if the polarity of the magnet is reversed, then the potential difference/current will be reversed too.
   - If you keep the magnet (or the coil) moving backwards and forwards, or keep it rotating in the same direction, you produce an alternating current (p.79).

2) You also get an induced p.d. when the magnetic field through an electrical conductor changes (gets bigger or smaller or reverses). This is what happens in a transformer (below).

3) You can increase the size of the induced p.d. by increasing the STRENGTH of the magnetic field, increasing the SPEED of movement/change of field or having MORE TURNS PER UNIT LENGTH on the coil of wire.

4) The induced p.d./current always opposes the change that made it:
   - When a current is induced in a wire, that current produces its own magnetic field (p.87).
   - The magnetic field created by an induced current always acts against the change that made it. Basically, it's trying to return things to the way they were.

Transformers Change the p.d. — but Only for Alternating Current

1) Transformers use induction to change the size of the potential difference of an alternating current.
2) They all have two coils of wire, the primary and the secondary coils, joined with an iron core.
3) When an alternating p.d. is applied across the primary coil, it produces an alternating magnetic field.
4) The iron in the core is a magnetic material (see p.86) that is easily magnetised and demagnetised. Because the coil is producing an alternating magnetic field, the magnetisation in the core also alternates.
5) This changing magnetic field induces a p.d. in the secondary coil.

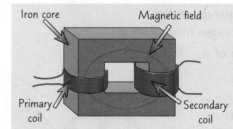

There's more about transformers on p.91.

STEP-UP TRANSFORMERS step the potential difference up (i.e. increase it). They have more turns on the secondary coil than the primary coil.

STEP-DOWN TRANSFORMERS step the potential difference down (i.e. decrease it). They have more turns on the primary coil than the secondary.

6) Transformers are almost 100% efficient. So you can assume that the input power is equal to the output power. Using $P = I \times V$ (page 78), you can write this as:

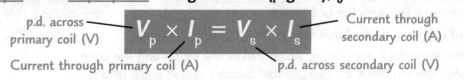

$$V_p \times I_p = V_s \times I_s$$

p.d. across primary coil (V) — Current through primary coil (A) — Current through secondary coil (A) — p.d. across secondary coil (V)

$V_p \times I_p$ is the power input at the primary coil. $V_s \times I_s$ is the power output at the secondary coil.

Transformers — NOT robots in disguise...

Make sure you know how transformers work, and then take a stab at using that equation with this question.

Q1 A transformer has an input potential difference of 1.6 V. The output power is 320 W.
    Calculate the input current.   [2 marks]

Generators, Microphones and Loudspeakers

Generators make use of electromagnetic induction from the previous page to induce a current. Whether this current is alternating or direct depends on exactly how the generator's put together.

Dynamos Generate Direct Current

1) Generators apply a force to rotate a coil in a magnetic field (or a magnet in a coil) — their construction is a lot like a motor.

2) As the coil (or magnet) spins, a current is induced in the coil. This current changes direction every half turn.

3) Dynamos are d.c. generators. They have a split-ring commutator (like a d.c. motor, p.88).

4) This swaps the connection every half turn to keep the current flowing in the same direction.

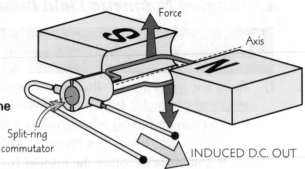

The current induced in an alternator or dynamo will be greater if there are more turns of wire in the coil, the magnetic flux density is increased or if the speed of rotation is increased.

Alternators Generate Alternating Current

1) Alternators work in the same way as dynamos, apart from one important difference.

2) Instead of a split-ring commutator, a.c. generators have slip rings and brushes so the contacts don't swap every half turn.

3) This means an alternator produces an alternating p.d. and therefore an alternating current (a.c.) if the coil is part of a complete circuit.

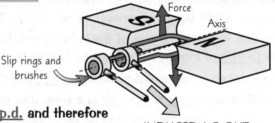

Microphones Generate Current From Sound Waves

1) Microphones use electromagnetic induction to generate an electrical signal.

2) Sound waves hit a flexible diaphragm that is attached to a coil of wire. The coil of wire surrounds one pole of a permanent magnet and is surrounded by the other pole.

3) This means as the diaphragm (and so the coil) moves, a current is generated in the coil.

4) The movement of the coil (and so the generated current) depends on the properties of the sound wave (louder sounds make the diaphragm move further).

5) This is how microphones can convert the pressure variations of a sound wave into variations in current in an electric circuit.

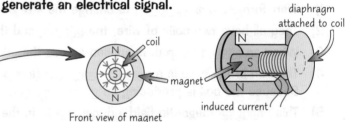

Loudspeakers are like Microphones in Reverse

1) In a loudspeaker, the diaphragm is replaced with a paper cone.

2) The coil is wrapped around one pole of a permanent magnet, so the a.c. signal causes a force on the coil (which moves the cone).

3) When the current is reversed, the force acts in the opposite direction.

4) These movements make the cone vibrate, which makes the air around the cone vibrate and creates the variations in pressure that cause a sound wave (p.35).

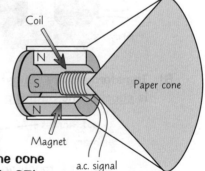

If a loudspeaker falls in the forest does it still make a sound...

Generators, microphones and loudspeakers all use electromagnetism — make sure you know how for the exam.

Q1 Explain how a loudspeaker converts electrical signals into sound waves. [4 marks]

Generating and Distributing Electricity

Now it's time for the big leagues — how electricity is generated and distributed on a national scale.

A Power Station uses a Turbine to Turn a Huge Alternator

1) Most of the electricity we use is generated from burning fuels (coal, oil, gas or biomass) in the boilers of big power stations.

2) The burning fuel is used to heat water and convert it to steam, which turns a turbine.

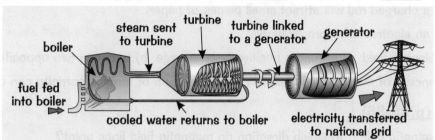

3) The turbine is connected to a powerful magnet (usually an electromagnet, see p.88) inside a generator — a huge cylinder wound with coils of copper wire.

4) As the turbine spins, the magnet spins with it, inducing a large p.d. and alternating current in the coils.

5) The coils are joined together in parallel (see p.75) to produce a single output from the generator.

6) A similar set-up is used for most other types of electricity generation as well. In hydroelectric, tidal and wind power (see p.29) the turbine is turned directly, without needing to turn water into steam first.

7) The only type of power generation that doesn't use a turbine and generator system is solar (p.29).

Transformers in the National Grid Produce a High p.d. and a Low Current

1) Once the electricity has been generated, it goes into the national grid — a network of wires and transformers that connects UK power stations to consumers (anyone who uses electricity).

2) The national grid has to transfer loads of energy each second, which means it transmits electricity at a high power (as power = energy transferred ÷ time taken, $P = E \div t$, p.78).

3) Electrical power = current × potential difference ($P = IV$, p.78), so to transmit the huge amounts of power needed, you either need a high potential difference or a high current.

4) But a high current makes wires heat up, so loads of energy is wasted to thermal stores. The power lost due to resistive heating is found using electrical power = current² × resistance ($P = I^2R$, p.78).

5) So to reduce these losses and make the national grid more efficient, high-voltage, low-resistance cables, and transformers are used. You saw on page 89 that transformers are (almost) 100% efficient, so the input power is equal to the output power. For a given power, as you increase the potential difference across a coil, you decrease the current through it ($V_p \times I_p = V_s \times I_s$).

6) Step-up transformers at power stations boost the p.d. up really high (400 000 V) and keep the current low. Step-down transformers then bring it back down to safe, usable levels at the consumers' end.

7) The ratio between the potential differences in the primary and secondary coils of a transformer is the same as the ratio between the number of turns on the coils.

8) So as long as you know the input p.d. and the number of turns on each coil, you can calculate the output p.d. from a transformer using the transformer equation:

Input p.d. (V)
Output p.d. (V)

$$\frac{V_p}{V_s} = \frac{N_p}{N_s}$$

Number of turns on primary coil
Number of turns on secondary coil

9) It works either way up, so $\frac{V_s}{V_p} = \frac{N_s}{N_p}$ works just as well.

I once had a dream about transforming into a hamster...

Make sure you can remember the stuff about transformers from page 89 too, then have a go at this question:

Q1   A transformer has 16 turns on its primary coil, 4 turns on its secondary coil and an output potential difference of 20 V. Calculate the potential difference across the primary coil.   [2 marks]

Revision Questions for Section 6

Congratulations! You've battled to the end of <u>Section 6</u> — now see how much you've learnt.

* Try these questions and <u>tick off each one</u> when you <u>get it right</u>.
* When you've done <u>all the questions</u> under a heading and are <u>completely happy</u>, tick it off.

Static Electricity and Electric Fields (p.82-84) ☑

1) How does the rubbing together of materials cause static electricity to build up? ☑
2) Explain why a charged rod will attract small pieces of paper. ☑
3) Explain how an electrostatic sprayer works. ☑
4) Sketch the electric field: a) around a positive point charge, b) between two oppositely-charged plates. ☑
5) Using the concept of electric fields, explain how a build up of static electricity can cause a spark. ☑

Magnetism (p.85-86) ☑

6) What is a magnetic field? In which direction do magnetic field lines point? ☑
7) Sketch the field lines around a bar magnet. ☑
8) Explain the behaviour of a plotting compass that is far away from a magnet. ☑
9) Give three examples of magnetic materials. ☑
10) What is the difference between a permanent magnet and an induced magnet? ☑

Electromagnetism and the Motor Effect (p.87-88) ☑

11) Describe the magnetic field around a current-carrying wire. ☑
12) Explain why a current-carrying conductor in a magnetic field experiences a force. ☑
13) State the equation for calculating the size of this force. ☑
14) What is Fleming's left-hand rule? ☑
15) Name two ways you could decrease the force on a current-carrying wire in a magnetic field. ☑
16) Explain how a basic d.c. motor works. ☑
17) Explain the shape and strength of the magnetic field inside and outside a solenoid. ☑

Electromagnetic Induction and Transformers (p.89-91) ☐

18) Describe how you can induce a current in a coil of wire. ☑
19) Give two ways you could reverse the direction of an induced current. ☑
20) Give one way that you can increase the size of an induced current. ☑
21) True or false? Induced currents create magnetic fields that oppose the change that made them. ☑
22) What kind of current are transformers used with? ☑
23) Why do transformers have a core of iron? ☑
24) True or false? Step-down transformers have more coils on their primary coil than on their secondary. ☑
25) A transformer has an input p.d. of 100 V and an output p.d. of 20 V. What kind of transformer is it? ☑
26) Write down the equation that relates the input and output currents and p.d.s of transformers.
    What does this equation assume? ☑
27) What kind of current do dynamos produce? ☑
28) Explain how microphones translate sound waves into electrical signals. ☑
29) Describe how a fossil fuel power station generates electricity. ☑
30) Explain how transformers are used to improve efficiency when transmitting electricity. ☑

Density

Time for some <u>maths</u> I'm afraid. But at least it comes with a fun experiment, so it's not all bad...

Density is Mass per Unit Volume

<u>Density</u> is a measure of the '<u>compactness</u>' (for want of a better word) of a substance. It relates the <u>mass</u> of a substance to how much <u>space</u> it <u>takes up</u>.

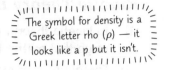

The symbol for density is a Greek letter rho (ρ) — it looks like a p but it isn't.

$$\text{Density} = \frac{\text{mass}}{\text{volume}}$$

$$\frac{m}{\rho \times V}$$

The units of density are g/cm^3 or kg/m^3.

1) The density of an object depends on what it's made of. Density <u>doesn't vary</u> with <u>size</u> or <u>shape</u>.

2) The average <u>density</u> of an object determines whether it <u>floats</u> or <u>sinks</u> — a solid object will <u>float</u> on a fluid if it has a <u>lower average density</u> than the fluid (p.102).

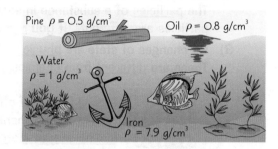

Pine $\rho = 0.5 \text{ g/cm}^3$
Oil $\rho = 0.8 \text{ g/cm}^3$
Water $\rho = 1 \text{ g/cm}^3$
Iron $\rho = 7.9 \text{ g/cm}^3$

You Can Find the Density of Solids and Liquids

1) To <u>find</u> the density of a substance, measure its <u>mass</u> and <u>volume</u> and use the formula above.

2) The easiest way to find the <u>density</u> of a <u>liquid</u> is to use a <u>measuring cylinder</u>.

3) Use a <u>mass balance</u> (p.104) to measure the <u>mass</u> of the <u>empty</u> measuring cylinder.

4) Pour in the liquid you're investigating. Measure the mass of the cylinder again — the <u>difference</u> in mass is equal to the <u>mass of the liquid</u>.

5) Finding the <u>volume</u> of the liquid is easy — just read it from the cylinder's scale. <u>1 ml = 1 cm^3</u>.

6) If you want to measure the volume of a <u>prism</u>, find the <u>area</u> of its <u>base</u> and then <u>multiply</u> it by its <u>height</u>. For a <u>cube</u> this is dead easy — it's just length × width × height.

7) If your object <u>isn't</u> a regular shape, you can find its volume using the fact that an object <u>submerged</u> in water will displace a volume of water <u>equal</u> to its <u>own volume</u>. One way of doing this is to use a <u>density bottle</u>:

PRACTICAL

1) Measure the <u>mass</u> (m_1) of the object using a mass balance.

2) <u>Fill</u> the bottle with a liquid of a <u>known density</u> (e.g. water).

3) Place the <u>stopper</u> into the bottle and <u>dry</u> the outside.

4) Measure the <u>mass</u> of the bottle (m_2).

5) <u>Empty</u> the bottle and place the <u>object</u> into the density bottle. Repeat steps 2 and 3. Measure the <u>mass</u> of the bottle (m_3).

6) Calculate the volume of displaced water:

- The <u>mass</u> of the <u>displaced water</u> = $m_2 - (m_3 - m_1)$

- You know the <u>density</u> of water, so you can use $V = m \div \rho$ to find the volume displaced. This equals the <u>volume of the object</u>.

7) Calculate the density of the object using $\rho = m \div V$ with the <u>mass</u> you measured in <u>step 1</u> (m_1) and the <u>volume</u> you calculated in <u>step 6</u>.

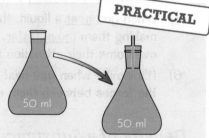

Liquid is pushed up the tube in the stopper, so the volume inside the bottle is constant.

You can also use a eureka can and a measuring cylinder if you don't have access to density bottles.

I'm feeling a bit dense after that lot...

Remember — density is all about how tightly packed the particles in a substance are. Nice and simple really.

Q1   An object has a mass of 0.45 kg and a volume of 75 cm^3. Calculate its density in kg/m^3.   [3 marks]

Q2   A cube has edges of length 1.5 cm and an average density of 3500 kg/m^3. What is its mass?   [3 marks]

Kinetic Theory and States of Matter

According to kinetic theory, everything's made of _tiny little balls_. The table, this book, your Gran...

Kinetic Theory is a Way of Explaining Matter

1) In kinetic theory, you can think of the particles that make up matter as _tiny balls_. You can explain the ways that matter behaves in terms of how these tiny balls _move_, and the _forces_ between them.

2) _Three states of matter_ are _solid_ (e.g. ice), _liquid_ (e.g. water) and _gas_ (e.g. water vapour). The _particles_ of a substance in each state are _the same_ — only the _arrangement_ and _energy_ of the particles are _different_. If you _reverse_ a change of state, the particles _go back_ to how they were before.

3) So changes of state are _physical changes_ (only the _form_ of a substance changes). These are _different_ from _chemical reactions_, where _new substances_ are created by the reaction.

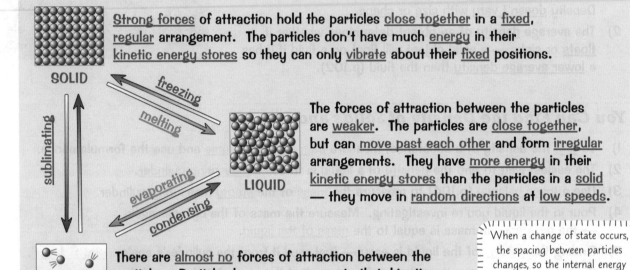

SOLID — _Strong forces_ of attraction hold the particles _close together_ in a _fixed_, _regular_ arrangement. The particles don't have much _energy_ in their _kinetic energy stores_ so they can only _vibrate_ about their _fixed_ positions.

LIQUID — The forces of attraction between the particles are _weaker_. The particles are _close together_, but can _move past each other_ and form _irregular_ arrangements. They have _more energy_ in their _kinetic energy stores_ than the particles in a _solid_ — they move in _random directions_ at _low speeds_.

GAS — There are _almost no_ forces of attraction between the particles. Particles have _more energy_ in their kinetic energy stores than those in _liquids_ and are _free to move_ — they travel in _random directions_ at _high speeds_.

When a change of state occurs, the spacing between particles changes, so the internal energy (see next page) of the substance also changes. As the particles get closer together, their internal energy decreases.

4) The _energy_ in a substance's _thermal energy_ store is held by its _particles_ in their _kinetic energy_ stores — this is what the thermal energy store actually is.

5) When you _heat_ a liquid, the _extra energy_ is transferred into the particles' _kinetic energy stores_, making them _move faster_. Eventually, when enough of the particles have enough energy to overcome their attraction to each other, big bubbles of _gas_ form in the liquid — this is _boiling_.

6) It's similar when you heat a _solid_. The extra energy makes the _particles vibrate faster_ until eventually the forces between them are _partly overcome_ and the particles start to move around — this is _melting_.

Density of a Substance Varies with State but Mass Doesn't

1) Provided you're working with a _closed system_ (i.e. no particles can escape, and no new particles can get in) the _mass_ of a substance _isn't affected_ when it changes _state_. This makes sense — the _mass of a substance_ is the _mass of its particles_, and the particles aren't changing, they're just being rearranged.

2) However, when a substance changes state its _volume does change_. The particles in most substances are _closer together_ when they're a _solid_ than a _liquid_ (ice and water are an exception), and are closer together when they're a _liquid_ than a _gas_ (see the diagrams above).

3) Since _density = mass ÷ volume_ (p.93), then density must change too. Generally, substances are _most dense_ when they're _solids_ and _least dense_ when they're _gases_.

Physics — it's really about state of mind...

Remember, the mass of a substance just comes from the particles, not the spaces between them. So as something expands or contracts, its volume changes but its mass stays the same.

Q1 Explain how the density of a typical substance changes as it changes from solid to liquid to gas. [3 marks]

Specific Heat Capacity

The <u>temperature</u> of something <u>isn't quite the same</u> thing as the <u>energy</u> stored in the substance's thermal energy store. That's where specific heat capacity comes in...

Specific Heat Capacity *Relates Temperature* and *Energy*

Internal energy is actually the sum of the energy in the kinetic and potential stores of the particles. You can usually ignore energy in potential stores though.

1) <u>Heating</u> a substance <u>increases</u> the <u>energy</u> in its <u>thermal energy store</u> (or the kinetic energy stores of its particles, see p.24). You may sometimes see this referred to as the <u>internal energy</u> of a substance.

2) So in kinetic theory, <u>temperature</u> is a way of measuring the <u>average internal energy</u> of a substance.

3) However, it takes <u>more energy</u> to <u>increase the temperature</u> of some materials than others. E.g. you need <u>4200 J</u> to warm 1 kg of <u>water</u> by 1 °C, but only <u>139 J</u> to warm 1 kg of <u>mercury</u> by 1 °C.

4) Materials that need to <u>gain</u> lots of energy to <u>warm up</u> also <u>release</u> loads of energy when they <u>cool down</u> again. They <u>store</u> a lot of energy for a given change in temperature.

5) The <u>change in the energy</u> stored in a substance when you heat it is related to the change in its <u>temperature</u> by its <u>specific heat capacity</u>. The <u>specific heat capacity</u> of a substance is the <u>change in energy</u> in the substance's thermal store needed to raise the temperature of <u>1 kg</u> of that substance by <u>1 °C</u>. E.g. water has a specific heat capacity of <u>4200 J/kg°C</u> (that's pretty high).

6) You need to know how to use the <u>equation</u> relating energy, mass, specific heat capacity and temperature.

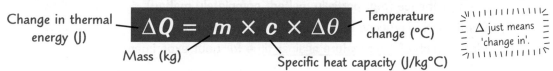

Change in thermal energy (J) ── $\Delta Q = m \times c \times \Delta \theta$ ── Temperature change (°C)

Mass (kg) ── ── Specific heat capacity (J/kg°C)

Δ just means 'change in'.

You can Find the Specific Heat Capacity of Water

PRACTICAL

You can use the experiment below to find the <u>specific heat capacity</u> of <u>water</u> — or any <u>liquid</u> for that matter. (There's another experiment on page 96 that investigates how water behaves when it <u>changes state</u>.)

If you can, you should use a <u>thermally insulated</u> container for both of these experiments to reduce <u>energy wasted to the surroundings</u> (p.27).

You can use this set up with solid blocks to find the SHC of solids.

1) Use a <u>mass balance</u> to measure the <u>mass</u> of the insulating container.

2) Fill the container with <u>water</u> and measure the <u>mass</u> again. The <u>difference</u> in mass is the mass of the <u>water in the container</u>.

3) Set up the experiment as shown — make sure the joulemeter reads <u>zero</u> and place a <u>lid</u> on the container if you have one.

4) Measure the <u>temperature</u> of the water, then turn on the power.

5) Keep an eye on the <u>thermometer</u>. When the temperature has increased by e.g. <u>ten degrees</u>, stop the experiment and record the <u>energy</u> on the joulemeter, and the <u>increase in temperature</u>.

6) You can then calculate the specific heat capacity of the water by <u>rearranging</u> the equation above, and plugging in your measurements.

7) <u>Repeat</u> the whole experiment at least three times, then calculate an <u>average</u> of the specific heat capacity (p.7).

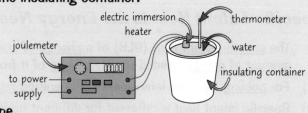

electric immersion heater — thermometer
joulemeter — water
to power supply — insulating container

You could also use a voltmeter and ammeter instead of a joulemeter, time how long the heater was on for, then calculate the energy supplied (p.77).

I wish I had a high specific fact capacity...

Make sure you practise using that equation — it's a bit of a tricky one.

Q1 If a metal has a specific heat capacity of 420 J/kg°C, calculate how much the temperature of a 0.20 kg block of the metal will increase by if 1680 J of energy are supplied to it. **[2 marks]**

Q2 Describe an experiment you could do to find the specific heat capacity of water. **[4 marks]**

Specific Latent Heat

If you heat up a pan of water on the stove, the water never gets any hotter than 100 °C. You can <u>carry on heating it up</u>, but the <u>temperature won't rise</u>. How come, you say? It's all to do with <u>latent heat</u>...

You Need to Put In Energy to Break Bonds Between Particles

1) Remember, when you <u>heat</u> a solid or liquid, you're transferring <u>energy</u> to the kinetic energy stores of the particles in the substance, making the particles <u>vibrate</u> or <u>move faster</u> (p.24).

2) When a substance is <u>melting</u> or <u>boiling</u>, you're still putting in <u>energy</u>, but the energy's used for <u>breaking bonds between particles</u> rather than raising the temperature.

3) When a substance is <u>condensing</u> or <u>freezing</u>, bonds are <u>forming</u> between particles, which <u>releases</u> energy. This means the <u>temperature doesn't go down</u> until all the substance has turned into a liquid (condensing) or a solid (freezing).

4) You can see this by doing this simple <u>experiment</u>:

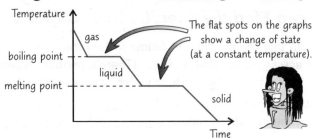

PRACTICAL

   1) Fill a <u>beaker</u> with <u>crushed ice</u>.
   2) Place a <u>thermometer</u> into the beaker and record the <u>temperature</u> of the ice.
   3) Using the Bunsen burner, <u>gradually heat</u> the beaker full of ice.
   4) Every twenty seconds, record the <u>temperature</u> and the <u>current state</u> of the ice (e.g. partially melted, completely melted).
   5) Continue this process until the water begins to <u>boil</u>.
   6) Plot a graph of <u>temperature against time</u> for your experiment.

thermometer
beaker — ice
stand
Bunsen burner

Your graph should look like this:

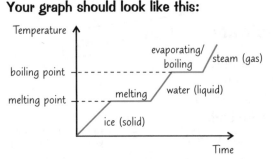

You get a similar one for <u>condensing</u> and <u>freezing</u>:

The flat spots on the graphs show a change of state (at a constant temperature).

Specific Latent Heat is the Energy Needed to Change State

$\nwarrow$ Don't get confused with specific heat capacity, which relates to a temperature rise of 1 °C.

1) The <u>specific latent heat</u> (SLH) of a <u>change of state</u> of a substance is the <u>amount of energy</u> needed to <u>change 1 kg</u> of it from <u>one state to another without changing its temperature</u>.

2) For <u>cooling</u>, specific latent heat is the energy <u>released</u> by a change in state.

3) Specific latent heat is <u>different</u> for <u>different materials</u>, and for changing between <u>different states</u>.

4) The specific latent heat for changing between a <u>solid</u> and a <u>liquid</u> (<u>melting</u> or <u>freezing</u>) is called the <u>specific latent heat of fusion</u>. The specific latent heat for changing between a <u>liquid</u> and a <u>gas</u> (<u>evaporating</u>, <u>boiling</u> or <u>condensing</u>) is called the <u>specific latent heat of vaporisation</u>.

5) You can work out the <u>energy needed</u> (or <u>released</u>) when a substance of mass *m* changes state using this <u>formula</u>:

Thermal Energy (Q) = Mass (m) × Specific Latent Heat (L)

$$\frac{Q}{m \times L}$$

Thermal energy is given in <u>joules</u> (<u>J</u>), mass is in <u>kg</u> and <u>SLH</u> is in <u>J/kg</u>.

Breaking Bonds — Blofeld never quite manages it...

Fun fact: this stuff explains how sweating cools you down — the energy that builds up in your body when you exercise is used to change liquid sweat into gas, rather than increasing your temperature. Nice...

Q1   Sketch a graph showing how the temperature of a sample of water will change over time as it's heated from −5 °C to 105 °C.   [3 marks]

Particle Motion in Gases

Gas particles fly around, bump into things and exert forces on them. This is happening to you right now — the air around you is exerting pressure on you (unless you're somehow reading this in space).

Colliding Gas Particles Create Pressure

1) According to kinetic theory, all matter is made up of very small, constantly moving particles.

2) Particles in a gas hardly take up any space. Most of the gas is empty space.

3) As the gas particles move about at high speeds, they bang into each other and whatever else happens to get in the way. When they collide with something, they exert a force (and so a pressure — p.101) on it.

4) In a sealed container, the outward gas pressure is the total force exerted by all of the particles in the gas on a unit area of the container walls.

A sealed container is an example of a closed system — no matter can get in or out.

Gas Pressure Varies with Volume and Temperature

1) The speed of gas particles depends on the temperature of the gas. The higher the temperature, the faster the particles move and the more often they collide with the container. The force exerted by each particle during a collision also increases as the temperature increases.

2) So increasing the temperature of a fixed volume of gas increases its pressure.

3) Alternatively, if temperature is constant, increasing the volume of a gas means the particles get more spread out and hit the walls of the container less often. The gas pressure decreases.

4) Pressure and volume are inversely proportional — when volume goes up, pressure goes down (and vice versa). For a gas of fixed mass at a constant temperature, the relationship is:

$$P_1V_1 = P_2V_2$$

where P_1 is the pressure at a volume V_1 and P_2 is the pressure at a volume V_2.
Pressure is in Pa (or N/m²) and volume is in m³.

Absolute Zero is as Cold as Stuff Can Get — 0 kelvin

1) If you increase the temperature of something, you give its particles more energy — they move about more quickly or vibrate more. In the same way, if you cool a substance down, you're reducing the energy of the particles.

2) In theory, the coldest that anything can ever get is -273 °C — this temperature is known as absolute zero. At absolute zero, the particles have as little energy in their kinetic stores as it's possible to get — they're pretty much still.

3) Absolute zero is the start of the Kelvin scale of temperature.

4) A temperature change of 1 °C is also a change of 1 kelvin. The two scales are pretty similar — the only difference is where the zero occurs.

5) To convert from degrees Celsius to kelvins, just add 273.
And to convert from kelvins to degrees Celsius, just subtract 273.

	Absolute zero	Freezing point of water	Boiling point of water
Celsius scale	–273 °C	0 °C	100 °C
Kelvin scale	0 K	273 K	373 K

There's no degree symbol when you write a temperature in kelvins. Just write K, not °K. OK.

Gas particles need to watch where they're going...

Remember, the more gas particles there are, and the faster they travel, the higher the pressure. Simple...

Q1 Find the value of 25 °C in kelvin. [1 mark]

Q2 Explain how a gas exerts pressure on its container. [2 marks]

Q3 3.5 m³ of a gas is at a pressure of 520 Pa. It is compressed to a volume of 1 m³ at a constant temperature. What is the new pressure of the gas? [3 marks]

Pressure, Temperature and Volume

Don't breathe out yet — there's <u>still more</u> about pressure that you need to know.

A Change in Pressure Can Cause a Change in Volume

1) You know from the previous page that a gas exerts a <u>force</u> on its container due to <u>collisions</u> between the particles and the walls of the container.

2) These collisions happen in <u>random directions</u>, but add together to produce a <u>net</u> (<u>overall</u>) <u>force</u> at <u>right angles</u> to the wall of the container.

3) Unless it's in a <u>vacuum</u>, the <u>outside</u> of a gas container will also be under <u>pressure</u> from <u>whatever's around it</u> — e.g. <u>atmospheric pressure</u> from the air (p.102).

4) For containers <u>without a fixed volume</u> (e.g. a balloon) the <u>volume</u> of the container (and so the volume of the gas inside) is <u>constant</u> (it <u>isn't expanding or contracting</u>) when the <u>pressure</u> of the gas <u>inside pushing outwards</u> is <u>equal to</u> the <u>pressure</u> of the air <u>outside pushing inwards</u>.

5) You can change the <u>volume of a gas</u> in a <u>container that doesn't have a fixed volume</u> by changing <u>either</u> the <u>internal</u> (<u>outward</u>) or <u>external</u> (<u>inward</u>) <u>pressure</u> on the container:

> You can change the <u>pressure</u> of a gas inside a container (e.g. a balloon) by <u>heating</u> or <u>cooling</u>.
>
> As the balloon is <u>heated</u>, the gas particles <u>inside it</u> gain <u>energy</u> and move around <u>quicker</u>. This <u>increases the pressure</u> of the gas inside the balloon.
>
> The <u>outward</u> pressure of the gas inside the balloon is now <u>larger</u> than the <u>inward</u> pressure caused by the <u>surroundings</u>. The <u>balloon</u> (and so the volume of the gas) <u>expands</u> until the pressures are <u>equal</u> once more.
>
> <u>Cooling</u> the gas in the balloon has the <u>opposite</u> effect — the <u>outward</u> pressure is <u>smaller</u> than the <u>inward</u> pressure, so the gas inside the balloon is <u>compressed</u>.

inward pressure from gas particles <u>outside</u> the balloon

outward pressure from gas particles <u>inside</u> the balloon

> You can change the <u>external pressure</u> on a gas in a number of ways:
>
> For a gas in an air-tight <u>syringe</u>, pushing hard on the <u>plunger</u> increases the <u>inward</u> pressure on the gas, so that it is larger than the outward pressure. This causes the gas inside of the syringe to be <u>compressed</u>.
>
> <u>Atmospheric pressure</u> (p.102) decreases as altitude increases, so as a container of gas <u>rises</u>, the <u>inward</u> pressure <u>decreases</u>. This causes the gas to <u>expand</u> as the altitude increases.

plunger

applied force increases inward pressure

syringe

Doing Work on a Gas Can Increase its Temperature

There's more about doing work on p.66.

1) <u>Doing work</u> on a gas can increase its <u>internal energy</u> (p.95), which increases its <u>temperature</u>.

2) You can do work on a gas <u>mechanically</u>, e.g. with a <u>bike pump</u>. (You also do work on a gas when you <u>heat it</u> up.)

3) The gas <u>exerts pressure</u> on the <u>plunger</u> of the pump, and so exerts a <u>force</u> on it. Work has to be done <u>against this force</u> to push down the plunger.

4) This transfers energy to the <u>kinetic energy stores</u> of the gas particles, so increases the <u>internal energy</u> and therefore the <u>temperature</u>.

5) If the pump is connected to e.g. a tyre, some of this energy is <u>transferred</u> from the gas to the <u>thermal energy store</u> of the tyre, and you'll feel the tyre getting <u>warmer</u> as you pump it up.

Hope the pressure's not getting to you...

Get your head around how changing pressure can cause a change in the volume of a gas (and its container).

Q1   Explain why pumping up a bike tyre increases the tyre's temperature.   [3 marks]

Forces and Elasticity

And now for something a bit more fun — <u>squishing</u>, <u>stretching</u> and <u>bending</u> stuff.

Stretching, Compressing or Bending Transfers Energy

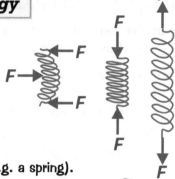

1) When you apply a force to an object you may cause it to <u>stretch</u>, <u>compress</u> or <u>bend</u>.

2) To do this, you need <u>more than one</u> force acting on the object (otherwise the object would simply <u>move</u> in the direction of the <u>applied force</u>, instead of changing shape).

3) An object has been <u>elastically distorted</u> if it can <u>go back</u> to its <u>original shape</u> and <u>length</u> after the force has been removed.

4) Objects that can be elastically distorted are called <u>elastic objects</u> (e.g. a spring).

5) An object has been <u>inelastically distorted</u> if it <u>doesn't</u> return to its <u>original shape</u> and <u>length</u> after the force has been removed.

6) The <u>elastic limit</u> is the point where an object <u>stops</u> distorting <u>elastically</u> and <u>begins</u> to distort <u>inelastically</u>.

Elastic objects — useful for passing exams and scaring small children

7) <u>Work is done</u> when a force stretches or compresses an object and causes energy to be transferred to the <u>elastic potential energy</u> store of the object. If it is <u>elastically distorted</u>, <u>ALL</u> this energy is transferred to the object's <u>elastic potential energy store</u> (see p.100).

Extension is Directly Proportional to Force...

If a spring is supported at the top and then a weight is attached to the bottom, it <u>stretches</u>.

1) The <u>extension</u> of a stretched spring (or other elastic object) is <u>directly</u> <u>proportional</u> to the load or <u>force</u> applied — so $F \propto x$.

2) This means that there is a <u>linear</u> relationship between force and extension. (If you plotted a <u>force-extension</u> graph for the spring, it would be a <u>straight line</u>.)

3) This is the equation: $$F = k \times x$$ where F is the applied force in N, k is the spring constant in N/m and x is the extension in m.

4) The <u>spring constant</u> depends on the <u>material</u> that you are stretching — a <u>stiffer</u> spring has a <u>greater</u> spring constant.

5) The equation also works for <u>compression</u> (where x is just the <u>difference</u> between the <u>natural</u> and <u>compressed</u> lengths — the <u>compression</u>).

For a linear relationship, the gradient of an object's force-extension graph is equal to its spring constant.

...but this Stops Working when the Force is Great Enough

There's a <u>limit</u> to the amount of force you can apply to an object for the extension to keep on increasing <u>proportionally</u>.

1) The graph shows <u>force against extension</u> for an elastic object.

2) There is a <u>maximum</u> force above which the graph <u>curves</u>, showing that extension is <u>no longer</u> proportional to force. The relationship is now <u>non-linear</u> — the object <u>stretches more</u> for each unit increase in force. This point is known as the <u>limit of proportionality</u> and is shown on the graph at the point marked P.

3) The <u>elastic limit</u> (see above) is marked as E. Past this point, the object is <u>permanently stretched</u>.

non-linear relationship

E
P

linear relationship

Force

Extension

I could make a joke, but I don't want to stretch myself...

That equation is pretty simple, but that doesn't mean you can skip over it. Have a go at the question below.

Q1 A spring is fixed at one end and a force of 1 N is applied to the other end, causing it to stretch. The spring extends by 2 cm. Calculate the spring constant of the spring. [2 marks]

Investigating Elasticity

You can do an easy _experiment_ to see exactly how adding _masses_ to a spring causes it to _stretch_.

You Can Investigate the Link Between Force and Extension PRACTICAL

Set up the apparatus as shown in the diagram. Make sure you have plenty of extra masses, then measure the _mass_ of each (with a mass balance) and calculate its _weight_ (the _force_ applied) using $W = mg$ (p.17).

You could do a quick _pilot experiment_ first to find out what size masses to use.

- Using an _identical spring_ to the one you will be testing, _load_ it with _masses_ one at a time and record the _force_ (weight) and _extension_ each time.
- Plot a _force-extension_ graph and check that you get a nice _straight line_ for at least the _first 6 points_. If it curves _too early_, you need to use _smaller masses_.

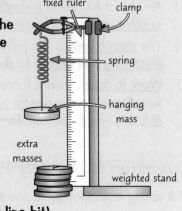

1) Measure the _natural length_ of the spring (when _no load_ is applied) with a _millimetre ruler_ clamped to the stand. Make sure you take the reading at eye level and add _markers_ (e.g. thin strips of tape) to the _top_ and _bottom_ of the spring to make the reading more accurate.

2) Add a mass to the spring and allow the spring to come to _rest_. Record the mass and measure the new _length_ of the spring. The _extension_ is the change in length.

3) _Repeat_ this process until you have enough measurements (no fewer than 6).

4) _Plot_ a _force-extension graph_ of your results. It will only start to _curve_ if you _exceed_ the _limit of proportionality_, but don't worry if yours doesn't (as long as you've got the straight line bit).

You should find that a _larger force_ causes a _bigger extension_. You can also think of this as _more work_ needing to be done to cause a larger extension. The _force_ doing work is the _gravitational force_ and for _elastic_ distortions, this force is _equal_ to $F = kx$.

You can find the _work done_ for a particular forces (or energy stored — see below) by calculating the _area_ under the _linear_ section of your _force-extension_ graph _up to_ that value of force.

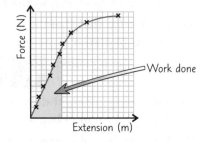

You Can Calculate Work Done for Linear Relationships

1) Look at the graph on the previous page. The _elastic limit_ is always _at_ or _beyond_ the _limit of proportionality_. This means that for a _linear relationship_, the distortion is always _elastic_ — all the energy being transferred is stored in the spring's _elastic potential energy store_.

2) So, as long as a spring is not stretched _past_ its _limit of proportionality_, _work done_ to the spring is _equal_ to the _energy_ stored in its elastic potential energy store.

3) For a linear relationship, the _energy_ in the _elastic potential energy store_ (and so the _work done_) can be found using:

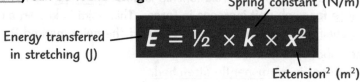

Spring constant (N/m)

Energy transferred in stretching (J) —— $E = \frac{1}{2} \times k \times x^2$

Extension² (m²)

Time to spring into action and learn all this...

Remember that you can only use the gradient to find the spring constant if the graph is linear (a straight line).

Q1   A spring with a spring constant of 40 N/m extends elastically by 2.5 cm.
      Calculate the amount of energy stored in its elastic potential energy store.   [2 marks]

Fluid Pressure

Hopefully reading this page will make you feel a little less _pressured_ about your physics exam.

Pressure is the Force per Unit Area

1) Pressure is the _force per unit area_.
The following equation can be used for _solids_, _liquids_ and _gases_:

$$P = \frac{F}{A}$$

Pressure in pascals (Pa)

Force normal to a surface (N)

Area of that surface (m²)

> The soles of high-heeled shoes have a small area, so they exert a large pressure on the ground, which can damage some types of flooring. The soles of snowshoes have very large areas, which 'spread out' your weight (the force) and stop you sinking into snow as you walk.

2) _Gases_ and _liquids_ are both _fluids_ (their particles are free to move, or '_flow_').

3) _Fluid pressure_ is the pressure caused by the _collisions_ of _gas_ or _liquid_ particles _on a given surface_.

4) Fluid pressure always exerts a _force_ at _right angles_ (_normal_) to any _surface_ in contact with the fluid (p.98).

5) The _force_ on a surface due to _fluid pressure_ depends on the _area_ of the object the fluid is in contact with.

6) The _properties_ of a fluid and the _atmospheric pressure_ surrounding the fluid affect _fluid pressure_ (see next page).

Fluid Pressure Depends on Depth and Density

1) _Density_ can be thought of as a measure of the '_compactness_' of a substance, i.e. how _close together_ the particles in a substance are. For a given _liquid_, the _density_ is _uniform_ (the _same everywhere_) and it _doesn't vary_ with _shape_ or _size_. The density of a _gas_ can vary though.

> Liquids can actually be squashed slightly under very large pressures, but because the change is so small you can assume the density of a liquid is uniform.

2) Assuming their particles have the _same mass_, a _denser_ fluid has _more particles_ in a certain space than a _less dense_ one. This means there are more particles that are able to _collide_ so the _pressure is higher_ at a given depth in the denser fluid.

3) As the _depth_ of a fluid increases, the number of particles _above_ that point increases. The _weight_ of these particles adds to the pressure felt at that point, so _fluid pressure_ increases with depth.

4) You can calculate the _pressure_ due to the _column_ of liquid _above_ a certain _depth_ using:

Height of the column (the depth) in m

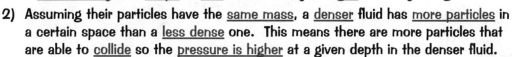

$$P = h \times \rho \times g$$

Pressure due to a column of liquid (Pa)

Gravitational field strength (N/kg)

Density of the liquid (kg/m³) (the symbol is the Greek letter 'rho')

EXAMPLE: Calculate the change in pressure between a point 20 m below the surface of water and a point 40 m below the surface. The density of water is 1000 kg/m³. The gravitational field strength of the Earth is 10 N/kg.

1) Calculate the _pressure_ caused by the water at a depth of _20 m_.

$P = h\rho g = 20 \times 1000 \times 10$
$= 200\ 000$ Pa

2) Do the same for a depth of _40 m_.

$P = h\rho g = 40 \times 1000 \times 10$
$= 400\ 000$ Pa

3) _Take away_ the pressure at _20 m_ from the pressure at _40 m_.

$400\ 000 - 200\ 000 = 200\ 000$ Pa (200 kPa)

> Check your answer makes sense (you can't get negative pressure).

So a gas is a fluid — next they'll be telling me custard is a solid...

Have another read through and make sure you can explain how pressure changes with depth.

Q1   Calculate the force exerted on a 10 m² area by a pressure of 200 kPa.   [2 marks]

Q2   At a point 5 cm below the surface of a jug of olive oil, the pressure is 450 Pa.
Calculate the density of olive oil. The gravitational field strength of Earth is 10 N/kg.   [2 marks]

Upthrust and Atmospheric Pressure

Fluid pressure can explain why potatoes sink and apples float. Because you've been dying to know...

Objects in Fluids Experience Upthrust

1) When an object is submerged in a fluid (either partially or completely), the pressure of the fluid exerts a force on it from every direction.

2) Pressure increases with depth, so the force exerted on the bottom of the object is larger than the force acting on the top of the object.

3) This causes a resultant force (p.67) upwards, known as upthrust.

4) The upthrust is equal to the weight of fluid that has been displaced by the object (e.g. the upthrust on an old boot in water is equal to the weight of a boot-shaped volume of water).

Pressure

Pressure

Spoon displaces this much water.

Upthrust is equal to the weight of this amount of water.

An Object Floats if its Weight = Upthrust

1) If the upthrust on an object is equal to the object's weight, then the forces balance and the object floats.

2) If an object's weight is more than the upthrust, the object sinks.

3) This means that whether or not an object will float depends on its density.

4) An object that is less dense than the fluid it is placed in displaces (pushes out of the way) a volume of fluid that is equal to its weight before it is completely submerged.

5) At this point, the object's weight is equal to the upthrust, so the object floats.

6) An object that is denser than the fluid it is placed in is unable to displace enough fluid to equal its weight. This means that its weight is always larger than the upthrust, so it sinks.

This much water weighs the same as the whole apple (because the apple is less dense than water).

The apple has displaced a volume of water equal to its weight so it floats.

This much water weighs less than a potato (because the potato is denser than water).

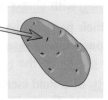

The potato can never displace a volume of water equal to its weight so it sinks.

Submarines make use of upthrust. To sink, large tanks are filled with water to increase the weight of the submarine so that it is more than the upthrust. To rise to the surface, the tanks are filled with compressed air to reduce the weight so that it's less than the upthrust.

Atmospheric Pressure Decreases with Height

1) The atmosphere is a layer of air that surrounds Earth. It is thin compared to the size of the Earth.

2) Atmospheric pressure is created on a surface by air molecules colliding with the surface.

3) As the altitude (height above Earth) increases, atmospheric pressure decreases — as shown on the graph. The graph is curved because atmospheric pressure is affected by the density of the atmosphere, which also varies with height.

4) As the altitude increases, the atmosphere gets less dense, so there are fewer air molecules that are able to collide with the surface.

5) There are also fewer air molecules above a surface as the height increases. This means that the weight of the air above it, which contributes to atmospheric pressure, decreases with altitude.

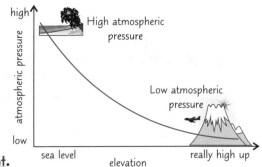

high

low

atmospheric pressure

High atmospheric pressure

Low atmospheric pressure

sea level   elevation   really high up

Next time you're feeling pressured, go on a hike...

Atmospheric pressure and liquid pressure are similar — but the density of the atmosphere changes (unlike liquids).

Q1   Explain why a wooden object (ρ = 700 kg/m^3) floats in water (ρ = 1000 kg/m^3).   [3 marks]

Revision Questions for Section 7

And you've reached the end of Section 7, woohoo — time to give your old grey matter a work out.

- Try these questions and tick off each one when you get it right.
- When you've done all the questions for a topic and are completely happy with it, tick off the topic.

Density and the Kinetic Theory of Matter (p.93-96) ☑

1) What is the formula for density? What are the units of density?
2) Briefly describe an experiment to find the density of a liquid.
3) For each state of matter, describe the arrangement of the particles.
4) Is a change of state a physical change or a chemical change?
5) Name five changes of state.
6) True or false? Mass stays the same when a substance changes state.
7) Define specific heat capacity.
8) Define specific latent heat. Give a formula for specific latent heat.

Gas Pressure (p.97-98) ☑

9) Define gas pressure for a sealed container.
10) What happens to the pressure of a gas in a sealed container of fixed volume when it is heated? Explain why this happens.
11) What is the relationship between pressure and volume at a constant temperature?
12) What is absolute zero? What value does it have in kelvin?
13) Describe how a change in external pressure can lead to a change in the volume of a gas in a sealed container.
14) True or false? Doing work on a gas can cause an increase in its temperature.

Stretching, Compressing and Bending (p.99-100) ☑

15) Explain why you need more than one force acting on an object to cause it to stretch.
16) What is the difference between an elastic and an inelastic distortion?
17) Give the equation that relates force, extension and the spring constant of an object.
18) How do you find the spring constant from a linear force-extension graph?
19) What is the limit of proportionality?
20) Draw a typical force-extension graph for an elastic object being stretched past its elastic limit.
21) Give the equation used to find the energy transferred in stretching an object.

Pressure and Upthrust (p.101-102) ☑

22) Define pressure and state the equation linking pressure, force and area.
23) True or false? Gases are fluids.
24) Explain how the pressure in a liquid varies with the density of the liquid.
25) True or false? Pressure in a liquid decreases with depth.
26) Give the equation for calculating the pressure due to a column of liquid.
27) Explain the cause of upthrust.
28) In what conditions will an object float?
29) What is atmospheric pressure?
30) True or false? Atmospheric pressure decreases as altitude increases.

Apparatus and Techniques

- This section covers <u>practical skills</u> you'll need to know about for your course.
- You'll have to do <u>8 core practicals</u> (experiments). These are covered earlier in the book and they're <u>highlighted</u> with <u>practical stamps</u> like this one.
- The following pages of this section cover some <u>extra bits and bobs</u> you need to know about practical work. First up, using apparatus to take measurements...

PRACTICAL

Mass Should Be Measured Using a Balance

1) For a <u>solid</u>, set the balance to <u>zero</u> and then place your object onto the scale and read off the mass.

2) If you're measuring the mass of a <u>liquid</u>, start by putting an empty container onto the <u>balance</u>. Next, <u>reset</u> the balance to zero.

3) Then just pour your <u>liquid</u> into the container and record the mass displayed. Easy.

Measure Most Lengths with a Ruler

1) In most cases a bog-standard <u>centimetre ruler</u> can be used to measure <u>length</u>. It depends on what you're measuring though — <u>metre rulers</u> or <u>long measuring tapes</u> are handy for <u>large</u> distances, while <u>micrometers</u> are used for measuring tiny things like the <u>diameter of a wire</u>.

2) The ruler should always be <u>parallel to</u> what you want to measure.

3) If you're dealing with something where it's <u>tricky</u> to measure just <u>one</u> accurately (e.g. water ripples, p.33), you can measure the length of e.g. <u>ten</u> of them and then <u>divide</u> to find the <u>length of one</u>.

4) If you're taking <u>multiple measurements</u> of the <u>same</u> object (e.g. to measure changes in length) then make sure you always measure from the <u>same point</u> on the object. It can help to put a <u>marker</u> or <u>pointer</u> onto the object to line up your ruler against.

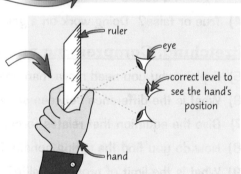

ruler
spring
pointer

5) Make sure the ruler and the object are always at <u>eye level</u> when you take a reading. This stops <u>parallax</u> affecting your results, e.g. if you're doing the ruler drop experiment (p.22).

6) <u>Parallax</u> is where a measurement appears to <u>change</u> based on <u>where you're looking from</u>. The <u>blue line</u> in the diagram on the right shows the <u>real position</u> of the <u>hand</u> relative to the <u>ruler</u>. If the eye <u>isn't level</u> with this line, it looks like the hand is <u>too low</u> or <u>too high</u>.

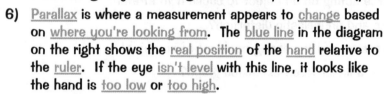

ruler
eye
correct level to see the hand's position
hand

Use a Protractor to Find Angles

1) First align the <u>vertex</u> (point) of the angle with the mark in the <u>centre</u> of the protractor.

2) Line up the <u>base line</u> of the protractor with one line that forms the <u>angle</u> and then measure the angle of the other line using the scale on the <u>protractor</u>.

3) If the lines creating the angle are very <u>thick</u>, align the protractor and measure the angle from the <u>centre</u> of the lines. Using a <u>sharp pencil</u> to trace light rays or draw diagrams helps to <u>reduce errors</u> when measuring angles.

4) If the lines are <u>too short</u> to measure easily, you may have to <u>extend</u> them. Again, make sure you use a <u>sharp pencil</u> to do this.

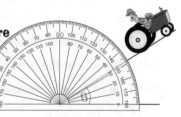

Measure Temperature Accurately with a Thermometer

bulb

1) Make sure the <u>bulb</u> of your thermometer is <u>completely submerged</u> in any substance you're measuring.

2) Wait for the temperature to <u>stabilise</u> before you take your initial reading.

3) Again, read your measurement off the <u>scale</u> on a thermometer at <u>eye level</u>.

When you're reading off a scale, use the value of the nearest mark on the scale (the nearest graduation).

Apparatus and Techniques

You May Have to Measure the Time Taken for a Change

1) You should use a <u>stopwatch</u> to <u>time</u> most experiments
— they're more <u>accurate</u> than regular watches.

2) Always make sure you <u>start</u> and <u>stop</u> the stopwatch at exactly
the right time. Or alternatively, set an <u>alarm</u> on the stopwatch so
you know exactly when to stop an experiment or take a reading.

3) You might be able to use a <u>light gate</u> instead (p.106).
This will <u>reduce the errors</u> in your experiment.

Measuring Cylinders and Pipettes Measure Liquid Volume

1) <u>Measuring cylinders</u> are the most common way to measure a liquid.

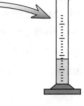

2) They come in all different <u>sizes</u>. Make sure you choose one that's the
<u>right size</u> for the measurement you want to make. It's no good using a
huge 1 dm³ cylinder to measure out 2 cm³ of a liquid — the graduations
(markings for scale) will be <u>too big</u> and you'll end up with <u>massive</u>
<u>errors</u>. It'd be much better to use one that measures up to 10 cm³.

3) You can also use a <u>pipette</u> to measure volume. <u>Pipettes</u> are used
to suck up and <u>transfer</u> volumes of liquid between containers.

4) <u>Graduated pipettes</u> are used to transfer <u>accurate</u> volumes.
A <u>pipette filler</u> is attached to the end of a graduated pipette,
to <u>control</u> the amount of liquid being drawn up.

5) Whichever method you use, always read the volume from the
<u>bottom of the meniscus</u> (the curved upper surface
of the liquid) when it's at <u>eye level</u>.

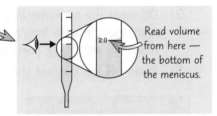

Read volume from here — the bottom of the meniscus.

Be Careful When You Do Experiments

1) There are always hazards in any experiment, so <u>before</u> you start an experiment you should read
and follow any <u>safety precautions</u> to do with your method or the apparatus you're using.

2) Stop masses and equipment falling by using <u>clamp stands</u>. Make sure masses are of a
<u>sensible weight</u> so they don't break the equipment they're used with, and use <u>pulleys</u> of a
sensible <u>length</u>. That way, any hanging masses won't <u>hit the floor</u> during the experiment.

3) When <u>heating</u> materials, make sure to let them <u>cool</u> before moving them, or wear <u>insulated gloves</u>
while handling them. If you're using an <u>immersion heater</u> to heat liquids, you should
always let it <u>dry out</u> in air, just in case any liquid has leaked inside the heater.

4) If you're using a <u>laser</u>, there are a few safety rules you must follow.
Always wear <u>laser safety goggles</u> and never <u>look directly into</u> the laser
or shine it <u>towards another person</u>. Make sure you turn the
laser <u>off</u> if it's not needed to avoid any accidents.

5) When working with electronics, make sure you use a <u>low</u> enough
<u>voltage</u> and <u>current</u> to prevent wires <u>overheating</u> (and potentially melting)
and avoid <u>damage to components</u>, like blowing a filament bulb.

6) You also need to be aware of <u>general safety</u> in the lab — handle
<u>glassware</u> carefully so it doesn't <u>break</u>, don't stick your fingers in
sockets and avoid touching frayed wires. That kind of thing.

Experimentus apparatus...

Wizardry won't help you here, unfortunately. Most of this'll be pretty familiar to you by now, but make sure you
get your head down and know these techniques inside out so they're second nature when it comes to any practicals.

Working with Electronics

Electrical devices are used in a bunch of experiments, so make sure you know how to use them.

You Have to Interpret Circuit Diagrams

Before you get cracking on an experiment involving any kind of electrical devices, you have to plan and build your circuit using a circuit diagram. Make sure you know all of the circuit symbols on page 71 so you're not stumped before you've even started.

There Are a Couple of Ways to Measure Potential Difference and Current

Voltmeters Measure Potential Difference

1) If you're using an analogue voltmeter, choose the voltmeter with the most appropriate unit (e.g. V or mV). If you're using a digital voltmeter, you'll most likely be able to switch between them.

2) Connect the voltmeter in parallel (p.75) across the component you want to test. The wires that come with a voltmeter are usually red (positive) and black (negative). These go into the red and black coloured ports on the voltmeter. Funnily enough.

3) Then simply read the potential difference from the scale (or from the screen if it's digital).

Ammeters Measure Current

1) Just like with voltmeters, choose the ammeter with the most appropriate unit.

2) Connect the ammeter in series (p.75) with the component you want to test, making sure they're both on the same branch. Again, they usually have red and black ports to show you where to connect your wires.

3) Read off the current shown on the scale or by the screen.

Turn your circuit off between readings to prevent wires overheating and affecting your results (p.72).

Multimeters Measure Both

1) Instead of having a separate ammeter and voltmeter, many circuits use multimeters. These are devices that measure a range of properties — usually potential difference, current and resistance.

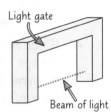

2) If you want to find potential difference, make sure the red wire is plugged into the port that has a 'V' (for volts).

3) To find the current, use the port labelled 'A' or 'mA' (for amps).

4) The dial on the multimeter should then be turned to the relevant section, e.g. to 'A' to measure current in amps. The screen will display the value you're measuring.

Light Gates Measure Speed and Acceleration

1) A light gate sends a beam of light (or sometimes infrared) from one side of the gate to a detector on the other side. When something passes through the gate, the beam of light is interrupted. The light gate then measures how long the beam was undetected.

2) To find the speed of an object, connect the light gate to a computer. Measure the length of the object and input this using the software. It will then automatically calculate the speed of the object as it passes through the beam.

3) To measure acceleration, use an object that interrupts the signal twice in a short period of time, e.g. a piece of card with a gap cut into the middle.

4) The light gate measures the speed for each section of the object and uses this to calculate its acceleration. This can then be read from the computer screen.

Have a look at page 18 for an example of a light gate being used.

Light gate

Beam of light

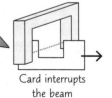

Card interrupts the beam

A light gate is better than a heavy one...

After finishing this page, you should be able to take on any electrical experiment that they throw at you... ouch.

Answers

p.12 — Distance, Displacement, Speed and Velocity

Q1 a) Any two from: e.g. speed / distance / mass / temperature *[2 marks]*

b) Any two from: e.g. displacement / momentum / force / acceleration / velocity *[2 marks]*

Q2 $s = d \div t = 200 \div 25$ *[1 mark]* = 8 m/s *[1 mark]*

p.13 — Acceleration

Q1 $u = 0$ m/s, $v = 5$ m/s, $a = g = 10$ m/s^2,
$x = (v^2 - u^2) \div 2a = (25 - 0) \div (2 \times 10)$ *[1 mark]*
= 1.25 m *[1 mark]*

p.14 — Distance/Time Graphs

Q1 E.g.

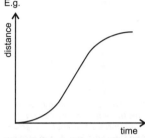

[1 mark for a continuous line that initially curves upwards, and which curves downwards at the end until it becomes horizontal, 1 mark for a straight middle section.]

p.15 — Velocity/Time Graphs

Q1 a)

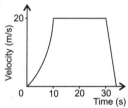

[1 mark for an upwards curved acceleration line to 20 m/s, 1 mark for a straight line representing steady speed, 1 mark for a straight line representing deceleration]

b) a = gradient of the line
= change in vertical ÷ change in horizontal
= $(0 - 20) \div (34 - 30)$ *[1 mark]*
= $-20 \div 4 = -5$ m/s^2
So the deceleration is 5 m/s^2 *[1 mark]*

p.16 — Newton's First and Second Laws

Q1 $F = ma = (80 + 10) \times 0.25$ *[1 mark]*
= 22.5 N *[1 mark]*

p.17 — Weight and Circular Motion

Q1 a) $W = mg = 25 \times 10$ *[1 mark]* = 250 N *[1 mark]*

b) $W = 25 \times 1.6$ *[1 mark]* = 40 N *[1 mark]*

p.18 — Investigating Motion

Q1 E.g. it removes human error for timings *[1 mark]*

p.19 — Inertia and Newton's Third Law

Q1 An object with a smaller mass (in this case the empty trolley) will have a smaller inertial mass, so less force is needed to stop it *[1 mark]*.

p.20 — Momentum

Q1 $p = mv = 60 \times 3$ *[1 mark]* = 180 kg m/s *[1 mark]*

Q2 Before the gun fires the bullet, the total momentum is zero (neither the gun nor the bullet are moving) *[1 mark]*. When the bullet leaves the gun, it has momentum in one direction *[1 mark]*. The gun moves backwards, and has an equal but opposite momentum to the bullet *[1 mark]*. This means that the total momentum after the bullet has been fired is still zero. Momentum has been conserved *[1 mark]*.

p.21 — Changes in Momentum

Q1 First, convert quantities to the correct units:
58 g = 0.058 kg
11.6 ms = 0.0116 s *[1 mark]*
$F = [(m \times v) - (m \times u)] \div t$
= $[(0.058 \times 34) - (0.058 \times 0)] \div 0.0116$
[1 mark]
F = 170 N *[1 mark]*

p.22 — Stopping Distances and Reaction Times

Q1 If you're tired, e.g. from a long journey, your reaction time is likely to be longer *[1 mark]*, which would increase thinking distance and so stopping distance *[1 mark]*. This would make an accident more likely if you needed to brake suddenly *[1 mark]*.

p.23 — Stopping Safely

Q1 For the lorry to stop the energy in the lorry's kinetic energy store must equal the work done by the brakes.
½ $mv^2 = Fd$ *[1 mark]*
so $F = mv^2 \div 2d$ *[1 mark]*
Estimate the mass of the lorry to be 30 000 kg (accept 15 000 - 45 000 kg) *[1 mark]*
$F = 30\ 000 \times 16^2 \div (2 \times 50) = 76\ 800$
= 80 000 N (to 1 s.f.)
(accept 40 000 - 100 000 N to 1 s.f.) *[1 mark]*

p.24 — Energy Stores

Q1 The change in height is 5 m.
So the energy transferred from the gravitational potential energy store is:
ΔGPE = $m \times g \times \Delta h = 2 \times 10 \times 5$ *[1 mark]*
= 100 J *[1 mark]*
This is transferred to the kinetic energy store of the object, so KE = 100 J *[1 mark]*
KE = ½ × $m \times v^2$ so $v^2 = (2 \times KE) \div m$
= $(2 \times 100) \div 2$ *[1 mark]*
= 100 m/s^2
$v = \sqrt{100}$ = 10 m/s *[1 mark]*

p.25 — Transferring Energy

Q1 Energy in the chemical energy store of the wood is transferred by heating to the thermal energy stores of the surroundings *[1 mark]*. The rest of the energy is transferred away by light waves *[1 mark]*.

p.26 — Efficiency

Q1 Useful energy transferred by device
= 500 – 420 = 80 J *[1 mark]*
Efficiency = $\dfrac{\text{useful energy transferred by device}}{\text{total energy supplied to device}}$
= 80 ÷ 500 = 0.16 *[1 mark]*
0.16 × 100 = 16% *[1 mark]*

p.27 — Reducing Unwanted Energy Transfers

Q1 E.g. lubricate moving parts *[1 mark]*.

p.28 — Energy Resources

Q1 Any two from: e.g. bio-fuels / wind power / the Sun/solar power / hydro-electricty / the tides *[2 marks]*

p.29 — More Energy Resources

Q1 E.g. wind farms produce no pollution, which is much better for the environment than burning coal. They are also cheap to run, as there are no fuel costs and minimal running costs.
You would need a lot of space to put the wind farm on, as you need lots of turbines to get the same power as a coal power station. People nearby also might dislike the wind farm, because wind farms spoil the view and can be noisy.
[4 marks — 1 mark for each correct advantage, up to 2 marks, 1 mark for each correct disadvantage, up to 2 marks].

p.30 — Trends in Energy Resource Use

Q1 Any two from: e.g. building new power plants is expensive / people don't want to live near new power plants / renewable energy resources are less reliable than non-renewable energy resources / hybrid cars are more expensive than equivalent petrol cars *[2 marks]*.

p.32 — Wave Basics

Q1 7.5 ÷ 100 = 0.075 m *[1 mark]*
$v = f\lambda$, so $f = v \div \lambda$
= 0.15 ÷ 0.075 *[1 mark]*
= 2 Hz *[1 mark]*

p.33 — Measuring Waves

Q1 E.g. attach a signal generator to a dipper and place it in a ripple tank filled with water to create some waves *[1 mark]*. Place a screen underneath the ripple tank, then turn on a strobe light and dim the other lights in the room *[1 mark]*. Adjust the frequency of the strobe light until the ripples appear to freeze *[1 mark]*. Measure the distance between the shadows on the screen beneath the tank — this is equal to the wavelength of the ripples *[1 mark]*.

p.34 — Wave Behaviour at Boundaries

Q1 The light will bend away from the normal *[1 mark]*.

p.35 — Sound

Q1 A sound wave enters the ear and causes the eardrum to vibrate *[1 mark]*. These vibrations are transmitted through the ear *[1 mark]* and turned into electrical signals which are sent to your brain *[1 mark]*.

p.36 — Ultrasound

Q1 $v = x \div t$,
so $t = x \div v$
= 2500 ÷ 1520 *[1 mark]*
= 1.64... s *[1 mark]*
This is the time it takes for the pulse to reach the seabed. To find the time taken for the sound to return to the submarine, you must double it.
1.64... × 2 = 3.28... = 3.3 s (to 2 s.f.) *[1 mark]*

p.37 — Infrasound and Seismic Waves

Q1 S-waves can only travel through solids *[1 mark]*. The S-waves can't travel though the centre of the Earth, so at least part of the Earth's core must be liquid *[1 mark]*.

p.38 — Reflection

Q1 specular *[1 mark]*

Q2

[1 mark for correct diagram showing straight, correctly drawn rays with consistent arrows and the normal, 1 mark for correct angle of incidence, 1 mark for correct angle of reflection]

p.39 — Investigating Refraction

Q1 a) Draw around a glass block onto a piece of paper. Shine a light ray from a ray box into the block *[1 mark]*. Trace the incident ray and mark where the ray emerges from the block. Remove the block and join these up with a straight line *[1 mark]*. Measure the angle of incidence and angle of refraction *[1 mark]*.

b) So you can easily trace the light ray to measure the angle between the ray and the normal *[1 mark]*.

p.40 — Visible Light and Colour

Q1 a) A cucumber looks green because it reflects green light *[1 mark]*, but absorbs all other wavelengths (colours) of light *[1 mark]*.

b) black *[1 mark]*

p.41 — Lenses

Q1 a) The point where rays hitting the lens parallel to the axis meet *[1 mark]*.

b) The point where light rays hitting the lens parallel to the axis appear to come from *[1 mark]*.

Q2

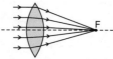

[1 mark for parallel lines being refracted and brought together as they pass through the lens, 1 mark for lines meeting at the principal focus (F)]

p.42 — Lenses and Ray Diagrams
Q1 virtual *[1 mark]*

Q2

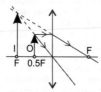

[1 mark for an image further away from the lense than 0.5F, 1 mark for an image where light rays cross, 1 mark for two correct light rays]

p.43 — Electromagnetic Waves
Q1 E.g. gamma rays are ionising so they can cause tissue damage and cancer, but visible light isn't ionising *[1 mark]*. They carry more energy than visible light, so their potential for damage is higher *[1 mark]*.

p.44 — Emitting and Absorbing EM Radiation
Q1 The bowl of ice cream is absorbing more power than it is radiating *[1 mark]*. This causes an increase in the temperature of the bowl of ice cream *[1 mark]*.

p.45 — EM Waves for Communication
Q1 They can pass easily through the Earth's watery atmosphere without being absorbed *[1 mark]*.

p.46 — Microwaves and Infrared
Q1 Any three from: e.g. burglar alarms / thermal imaging / short range communication / cooking / optical fibres *[3 marks]*

p.47 — More Uses of EM Waves
Q1 Any two from: e.g. fluorescent lamps / security pens / detecting forged bank notes / sterilising water *[2 marks]*

Q2 E.g. you don't have to freeze it/cook it/preserve it to keep it fresher for longer *[1 mark]*

p.49 — The Model of the Atom
Q1 a) The centre of an atom is a tiny, positively charged nucleus *[1 mark]*. This is made up of protons and neutrons and is the source of most of the atom's mass *[1 mark]*. Most of the atom is empty space *[1 mark]*. Electrons orbit the nucleus at set energy levels *[1 mark]*.

b) The radius of a nucleus is about 10 000 times smaller than the radius of the atom *[1 mark]*.

p.50 — Electron Energy Levels
Q1 A positive ion is an atom that has lost one or more electrons *[1 mark]*. A positive ion is formed when an outer electron absorbs enough energy that it leaves the atom *[1 mark]*.

p.51 — Isotopes and Nuclear Radiation
Q1 E.g. a thin sheet of paper will absorb alpha particles *[1 mark]*. Aluminium that's about 5 mm thick will absorb beta-minus particles *[1 mark]*. Thick sheets of lead or many metres of concrete will absorb gamma rays *[1 mark]*.

p.52 — Nuclear Equations
Q1 Beta-minus particle *[1 mark]*

Q2 $^{219}_{86}Rn \rightarrow \,^{215}_{84}Po + \,^{4}_{2}\alpha$
[1 mark for correct layout, 1 mark for correct symbol for an alpha particle, 1 mark for total atomic and mass numbers being equal on both sides]

p.53 — Half-Life
Q1 The number of half-lives in 240 hours is
240 ÷ 60 = 4 half-lives *[1 mark]*
Initial count = 480
after 1 half-life = 480 ÷ 2 = 240
after 2 half-lives = 240 ÷ 2 = 120
after 3 half-lives = 120 ÷ 2 = 60
after 4 half-lives = 60 ÷ 2 = 30
So the activity after 240 hours = 30 Bq *[1 mark]*

p.54 — Background Radiation and Contamination
Q1 E.g. rocks *[1 mark]*, cosmic rays *[1 mark]* and fallout from nuclear explosions *[1 mark]*

p.55 — Uses of Radiation
Q1 Alpha radiation is highly ionising so would damage cells in the body *[1 mark]*. Alpha radiation can't penetrate through tissue, so it wouldn't be detected outside the body with the radiation detector *[1 mark]*.

p.56 — PET Scanning and Radiotherapy
Q1 The patient is injected with a substance that contains a radioactive isotope *[1 mark]*. This isotope decays and produces positrons which annihilate with nearby electrons and produce gamma rays *[1 mark]*. These gamma rays are then detected outside of the body *[1 mark]*. Areas of high metabolism (where there are lots of gamma rays produced) can indicate the presence of a cancerous tumour *[1 mark]*.

p.57 — Nuclear Fission
Q1

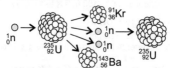

[3 marks for a labelled diagram — 1 mark for showing a neutron being absorbed to cause splitting, 1 mark for a large nucleus splitting into two smaller nuclei, 1 mark for it producing a neutron that is absorbed by another large, unstable nucleus.]

p.58 — Nuclear Fusion and Nuclear Power
Q1 All nuclei have a positive charge, so when they are close they repel each other *[1 mark]*. High pressures and temperatures are needed to overcome this electrostatic repulsion and fuse the two nuclei together *[1 mark]*.

p.59 — The Solar System and Gravity
Q1 a) almost circular orbits around the Sun *[1 mark]*
b) almost circular orbits around planets *[1 mark]*
c) highly elliptical orbits around the Sun *[1 mark]*

p.60 — Changing Ideas about the Universe
Q1 In the geocentric model, everything in our Solar System orbits the Earth. In the heliocentric model, everything orbits the Sun *[1 mark]*.

Q2 E.g. the Big Bang theory puts a finite age on the Universe, whereas the Steady State theory assumes there is no beginning and no end to the Universe *[1 mark]*.
In the Steady State theory, matter is constantly being created. In the Big Bang theory, all of the matter in the Universe occupied a small, dense region of space at the start of the Universe, which then 'exploded' outwards *[1 mark]*.

p.61 — Red-shift and CMB Radiation
Q1 E.g. red-shift is where the light we see from distant galaxies appears at a lower frequency than we would expect *[1 mark]*.

Q2 The Big Bang theory *[1 mark]*

p.62 — The Life Cycle of Stars
Q1 E.g. a cloud of dust and gas (nebula) is attracted together by gravity, forming a protostar *[1 mark]*. As the star gets denser, it gets hotter and hotter, until nuclear fusion of hydrogen nuclei starts to happen in its core *[1 mark]*. This nuclear fusion provides an outward pressure to balance the force of gravity, so the star remains a stable size, as a main sequence star *[1 mark]*. When the star runs out of hydrogen to fuse, it will expand and cool, becoming a red supergiant *[1 mark]*. It begins to glow brightly again and expands and contracts several times

until it explodes in a supernova *[1 mark]*. The supernova throws dust and gas into space and leaves behind either a very dense core called a neutron star or a black hole if it is massive enough *[1 mark]*.

p.63 — Looking Into Space
Q1 Any three from: e.g. move the telescope to a darker location / move the telescope to a higher location / use a telescope with a larger aperture / use a higher quality objective lens *[3 marks]*.

p.65 — Energy Transfers and Systems
Q1 The wind does work on the windmill *[1 mark]* causing it to turn and transferring energy to the kinetic energy store of the windmill *[1 mark]*.

p.66 — Work Done and Power
Q1 $E = F \times d = 20 \times 0.2$ *[1 mark]* = 4 N *[1 mark]*
Q2 $P = E \div T = 6000 \div 30$ *[1 mark]*
= 200 W *[1 mark]*

p.67 — Forces
Q1 E.g.

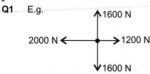

[2 marks for all forces correctly drawn, 1 mark for three forces correctly drawn — weight and normal contact force arrows should be the same length, the arrow for the driving force should be longer than the weight arrow and the arrow for the resistive force should be shorter]

p.68 — Forces and Vector Diagrams
Q1 E.g.

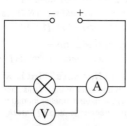

Resultant force = 13 N
[1 mark for a correct scale drawing, 1 mark for correct resultant force]

p.69 — Moments
Q1 moment of a force = force × distance normal to the direction of the force
= 10 × 0.85 *[1 mark]* = 8.5 Nm *[1 mark]*

p.71 — Current and Circuits
Q1 $Q = I \times t$, so
$t = Q \div I = 120 \div 2.5$ *[1 mark]*
= 48 s *[1 mark]*

p.72 — Potential Difference and Resistance
Q1 $E = Q \times V$, so
$V = E \div Q = 360 \div 75$ *[1 mark]*
= 4.8 V *[1 mark]*

p.73 — Investigating Components
Q1

[1 mark for a complete circuit with a variable d.c. power supply in series with a filament lamp, 1 mark for correct circuit symbols for all components, 1 mark for a voltmeter connected across the filament lamp and an ammeter connected in series with the filament lamp.]

p.74 — Circuit Devices
Q1 a) E.g. automatic night lights — a light automatically turns on when it gets dark *[1 mark]*.
b) E.g. thermostats — the heating automatically turns on/off at a certain temperature *[1 mark]*.

p.75 — Series and Parallel Circuits
Q1 0.5 A *[1 mark]*

Q2 E.g.

[1 mark for the correct circuit symbols, 1 mark for two bulbs connected in parallel, 1 mark for both switches being on the same branches as the lamps]

p.76 — More on Series and Parallel Circuits
Q1 $R = 2 + 3 + 7 = 12\ \Omega$ *[1 mark]*
$I = V \div R = 12 \div 12$ *[1 mark]* = 1 A *[1 mark]*

p.77 — Energy in Circuits
Q1 $E = I \times V \times t = 8.0 \times 230 \times (60 \times 60)$ *[1 mark]*
= 6 624 000 J *[1 mark]*

p.78 — Power in Circuits
Q1 $E = P \times t = 250 \times (2 \times 60 \times 60)$
= 1 800 000 J *[1 mark]*
$E = 375 \times (2 \times 60 \times 60) = 2\ 700\ 000$ J *[1 mark]*
So difference in the energy transferred is
2 700 000 − 1 800 000 = 900 000 J *[1 mark]*

p.79 — Electricity in the Home
Q1 In alternating current supply, the movement of the charges is constantly changing direction *[1 mark]*. In a direct current supply, the movement of the charges is only in one direction *[1 mark]*.

p.80 — Fuses and Earthing
Q1 The live wire *[1 mark]*.

p.82 — Static Electricity
Q1 As the jumper rubs against her shirt, a static charge builds up on both the jumper and the shirt *[1 mark]*. This is due to electrons being removed from one and being deposited onto the other *[1 mark]*. The charge becomes large enough for electrons to 'jump' across the small air gap between the jumper and the shirt, causing sparks *[1 mark]*.

p.83 — Uses and Dangers of Static Electricity
Q1 Any two from: e.g. photocopiers / reducing pollution/smoke / painting cars / electrostatic sprayers / spraying insecticide
[2 marks — 1 mark for each correct use]

p.84 — Electric Fields
Q1

[1 mark for at least 8 straight lines at right angles to the surface, 1 mark for arrows on the lines pointing away from the sphere, 1 mark for lines equally spaced]

p.85 — Magnets and Magnetic Fields
Q1

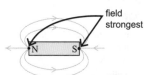

[1 mark for at least two lines from north to south, 1 mark for an arrow on a line pointing from north to south, 1 mark for an indication of the field being strongest at the poles]

Q2
Put the magnet on a piece of paper and put a compass next to it, making a mark on the paper at each end of the needle *[1 mark]*. Then move the compass so that the tail of the compass needle is where the tip of the needle was previously, and mark again where the needle is pointing *[1 mark]*. Repeat this several times and then join up the markings for a complete sketch of a field line around the magnet *[1 mark]*. Do this several times for different points around the magnet to get several field lines *[1 mark]*.

p.86 — Permanent and Induced Magnets
Q1 Any three from: e.g. fridge doors / speakers / microphones / doorbells / cranes *[3 marks]*

Q2 E.g. permanent magnets produce their own magnetic fields but induced magnets become magnets when they're in a magnetic field *[1 mark]*. The force between an induced magnet and a permanent magnet is always attractive, but between two permanent magnets it can be attractive or repulsive *[1 mark]*.

p.87 — Electromagnetism and the Motor Effect
Q1 Rearrange $F = B \times I \times l$
for the magnetic flux density, B:
$B = F \div (I \times l)$
$= 0.98 \div (5.0 \times 0.35)$ *[1 mark]*
= 0.56 T (or N/Am) *[1 mark]*

p.88 — Motors and Solenoids
Q1

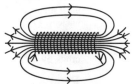

[1 mark for tightly packed lines inside the coil, 1 mark for parallel lines inside the coil, 1 mark for field similar to a bar magnet outside of coil]

p.89 — Electromagnetic Induction in Transformers
Q1 $V_p \times I_p = V_s \times I_s = 320$ W
$I_p = 320 \div V_p = 320 \div 1.6$ *[1 mark]*
= 200 A *[1 mark]*

p.90 — Generators, Microphones and Loudspeakers
Q1 A coil of wire is attached to a paper cone and then placed over one pole of a permanent magnet (whilst being surrounded by the second pole) *[1 mark]*. When a current flows through the wire, this causes a force which moves the cone forwards *[1 mark]*. When the current is reversed, the force is reversed and the cone is moved backwards *[1 mark]*. By changing the current, the cone can be made to vibrate, which vibrates the air around it to create a sound wave *[1 mark]*.

p.91 — Generating and Distributing Electricity
Q1 $V_p \div V_s = N_p \div N_s$
$V_p = (N_p \div N_s) \times V_s$
$= (16 \div 4) \times 20$ *[1 mark]* = 80 V *[1 mark]*

p.93 — Density
Q1 volume in $m^3 = 75 \div (100^3)$
$= 7.5 \times 10^{-5}\ m^3$ *[1 mark]*
density = mass ÷ volume
$= 0.45 \div (7.5 \times 10^{-5})$ *[1 mark]*
$= 6000\ kg/m^3$ *[1 mark]*

Q2 First find the cube's volume:
$0.015 \times 0.015 \times 0.015 = 3.375 \times 10^{-6}\ m^3$ *[1 mark]*
The cube's density is 3500 kg/m³.
$m = \rho \times V = 3500 \times (3.375 \times 10^{-6})$ *[1 mark]*
= 0.01181... kg = 12 g (to 2 s.f.) *[1 mark]*

p.94 — Kinetic Theory and States of Matter
Q1 As a typical substance changes from solid to liquid to gas, its density will decrease *[1 mark]* as its mass will stay the same *[1 mark]* but its volume will increase as the particles have more energy to overcome the forces between them *[1 mark]*.

p.95 — Specific Heat Capacity
Q1 $\Delta Q = mc\Delta\theta$, so:
$\Delta\theta = \Delta Q \div (m \times c)$
$= 1680 \div (0.20 \times 420)$ *[1 mark]*
= 20 °C *[1 mark]*

Q2 E.g. measure the mass of an empty insulating container. Pour water into the container and measure the mass again. Use this to determine the mass of the water *[1 mark]*. Using an immersion heater connected to a joulemeter, heat the water *[1 mark]*. Use a thermometer to monitor the temperature of the water. Once the temperature of the water has increased by 10 °C, turn off the immersion heater *[1 mark]*. Use the reading from the joulemeter and the equation $\Delta Q = mc\Delta\theta$ to find the specific heat capacity *[1 mark]*.

p.96 — Specific Latent Heat
Q1

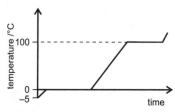

*[1 mark for showing the line as flat at 0 °C, 1 mark for showing the line as flat at 100 °C.
1 mark for drawing the line as straight, with a positive gradient, for temperatures below 0 °C, between 0 and 100 °C, and above 100 °C.]*

p.97 — Particle Motion in Gases
Q1 25 + 273 = 298 K *[1 mark]*

Q2 When gas particles collide with the walls of their container, they exert a force on it *[1 mark]*. Across many particles, this force acting on the container causes an outward pressure *[1 mark]*.

Q3 $P_1V_1 = P_2V_2$, so when $V_1 = 3.5\ m^3$,
$P_1V_1 = 520 \times 3.5 = 1820$ *[1 mark]*
When $V_2 = 1\ m^3$,
$P_2V_2 = P_2 \times 1 = 1820$ *[1 mark]*,
so $P_2 = 1820$ Pa *[1 mark]*

p.98 — Pressure, Temperature and Volume
Q1 Gas particles in the tyre exert a force on the plunger of the pump, so work must be done against this force to push down the pump *[1 mark]*. This transfers energy to the kinetic energy stores of the gas particles, increasing their internal energy *[1 mark]*. Temperature is a measure of the internal energy of the particles in a system, so this means the temperature of the gas (and therefore the tyre) increases *[1 mark]*.

p.99 — Forces and Elasticity
Q1 $k = F \div x = 1 \div 0.02$ *[1 mark]* = 50 N/m *[1 mark]*

p.100 — Investigating Elasticity
Q1 $E = \frac{1}{2}kx^2 = \frac{1}{2} \times 40 \times (0.025)^2$ *[1 mark]*
= 0.0125 J *[1 mark]*

p.101 — Fluid Pressure
Q1 $F = P \times A = 200\ 000 \times 10$ *[1 mark]*
= 2 000 000 N *[1 mark]*

Q2 $P = h\rho g$ so $\rho = P \div gh$
$\rho = 450 \div (10 \times 0.05)$ *[1 mark]*
$\rho = 900\ kg/m^3$ *[1 mark]*

p.102 — Upthrust and Atmospheric Pressure
Q1 Wood is less dense than water *[1 mark]*, which means that when a wooden object is placed in water, it can displace enough water to create an upthrust equal to the weight of the object *[1 mark]*. So the upthrust equals the weight and it floats *[1 mark]*.

Index